IT'S TIME FOR
E A S T E R

WRITTEN AND COMPILED BY

Elizabeth Hough Sechrist and Janette Woolsey

Illustrations by Elsie Jane McCorkell

MACRAE SMITH COMPANY: PHILADELPHIA

ACKNOWLEDGMENTS

The authors wish to express their thanks and appreciation to the following authors and publishers for their kind permission to include their works in this volume:

Francesco M. Bianco for "The Apple Tree" by Margery Williams Bianco; Mrs. Mary Alice Bigham for "Why the Ivy Is Always Green" by Madge Bigham; The Bobbs-Merrill Company, Inc. for "The Boy Who Discovered the Spring" from WHY THE CHIMES RANG AND OTHER STORIES by Raymond Macdonald Alden, copyright 1906, 1934, 1954, used by special permission of the publishers, The Bobbs-Merrill Company, Inc.; Mr. Padraic Colum for "The White Blackbird" by Padraic Colum from his book THE PEEP-SHOW MAN, copyright 1924; Elizabeth Yates McGreal and Coward-McCann, Inc. for "Bringing In the Spring" from UNDER THE LITTLE FIR AND OTHER STORIES by Elizabeth Yates; copyright and published 1942 by Coward-McCann, Inc., used by permission; Miss N. Carr Grace and the Junior Red Cross News for "Easter in the Woods" by Frances Frost; Henry Holt and Company, Inc. for "A Prayer in Spring" by Robert Frost, from COMPLETE POEMS OF ROBERT FROST, copyright 1930, 1949, by Henry Holt and Company, Inc., and for "The Lent Lily" by A. E. Housman, from COMPLETE POEMS by A. E. Housman, copyright 1940, 1959 by Henry Holt and Company, Inc., by permission of the publishers; The Horn Book, Inc. for "Pasque" by Ella Young, reprinted from Horn Book; Houghton Mifflin Company for "Song of Easter" by Celia Thaxter, used by courtesy of the publisher, Houghton Mifflin Company; Eleanore M. Jewett for "Even Unto the End of the World"; Little, Brown & Company for "At Easter Time" by Laura E. Richards from her book IN MY NURSERY, used by courtesy of the publisher, Little, Brown &

acknowledgments continued

Company; Longmans, Green & Company, Inc. for "Candles at Midnight" by Alice Geer Kelsey from her book RACING THE RED SAIL, copyright 1947, published by Longmans, Green & Company; The Ohio Society for Crippled Children, Inc. for the quotation from "The Daddy Allen Story"; The Pennsylvania Society for Crippled Children and Adults, Inc. for material on the Easter Seal Society; Aileen Fisher and Plays, Inc. for "Easter Morn" by Aileen Fisher; "Easter Morn," copyright 1953 by Aileen Fisher has been reprinted from HOLIDAY PROGRAMS FOR BOYS AND GIRLS, published by Plays, Inc., Boston, Mass.; Albert Whitman & Company for "Secrets of the Mardi Gras" by Joan and Josephine Costantino, published by Albert Whitman & Company.

In collecting the material used in this anthology every effort has been made to find the copyright owners of the material used. The editors hope they will be notified if anyone has been overlooked so that correction can be made.

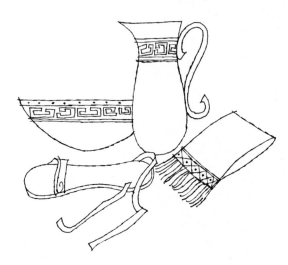

To

ELIZABETH ELLEN THOMPSON

and

ANN HARK

PREFACE

Easter and Christmas are the two most significant days observed in the Christian Church. But to children, the celebration of Christmas usually has more meaning than that of Easter. And it is for this reason that we have attempted to explain some of the Easter customs that have grown up around its celebration and to relate them to the true meaning of the day. Little children associate the word Easter with Easter bunnies and gay-colored eggs. But as they grow older and hear the story of the first Easter, they ask questions. "How did the custom of bunnies and eggs start?" "Why do people in some parts of the world observe Fastnacht Day?" "Why doesn't Easter come on the same day each year?"

In IT'S TIME FOR EASTER, we have answered these questions and many others concerning Easter customs. We have also tried to show that Easter itself is the climax of the season which just precedes it. We have included Mardi Gras and Lent because these, too, are a part of the Easter story. For the same reason, we have presented music, legends, the Oberammergau Passion Play, and the story of the Easter Seal. The poetry and stories selected include not only those which are of Easter Day but also those telling of the coming of Spring—the rebirth of living things.

We hope the book may be found useful and will add something to the understanding of Easter. And when we hear, on that happy morning, voices joyfully singing, "Jesus Christ is risen today," we can answer, "Truly, He is risen."

ELIZABETH HOUGH SECHRIST

JANETTE WOOLSEY

CONTENTS

The Easter Story

THE EASTER STORY AS TOLD IN THE GOSPELS ACCORDING
TO ST. MATTHEW, ST. MARK, ST. LUKE, AND ST. JOHN   19

THE HISTORY OF EASTER *by Elizabeth Hough Sechrist*   21

Easter Customs by Elizabeth Hough Sechrist

THE DAYS OF LENT   31

EASTER AROUND THE WORLD   46

IN THE EASTER BASKET   60

Easter Legends by Janette Woolsey

SYMBOLS AND LEGENDS   71

THE QUEST OF THE HOLY GRAIL   91

Easter Music by Janette Woolsey

THE MUSIC OF EASTER   103

GEORGE FRIDERIC HANDEL AND "MESSIAH"   105

JOHANN SEBASTIAN BACH AND THE ST. MATTHEW PASSION   111

RICHARD WAGNER AND PARSIFAL   116

THE PALMS   124

RIDE ON, RIDE ON IN MAJESTY   126

IN THE CROSS OF CHRIST I GLORY   128

MY FAITH LOOKS UP TO THEE   130

JESUS CHRIST IS RIS'N TODAY   132

THE STRIFE IS O'ER   135

CONTENTS

Easter Poems

PASQUE *by Ella Young*   141

SONG *by Charles G. Blanden*   141

A PRAYER IN SPRING *by Robert Frost*   142

SONG OF EASTER *by Celia Thaxter*   143

GREEN THINGS GROWING *by Dinah Maria Mulock*   144

EASTER IN THE WOODS *by Frances Frost*   145

SONG *by Henry Neville Maugham*   145

THE LENT LILY *by A. E. Housman*   146

EASTER *by Edwin L. Sabin*   147

AT EASTER TIME *by Laura E. Richards*   148

EASTER WEEK *by Charles Kingsley*   149

SHEEP AND LAMBS *by Katharine Tynan Hinkson*   150

BALLAD OF TREES AND THE MASTER *by Sidney Lanier*   151

THE ORIGIN OF THE EASTER LILIES *Unknown*   152

JOY FROM "HUMANITAD" *by Oscar Wilde*   153

EASTER MORN *by Aileen Fisher*   154

Easter Stories

EVEN UNTO THE END OF THE WORLD
    by Eleanore M. Jewett   159

THE WHITE BLACKBIRD *by Padraic Colum*   170

THE BOY WHO DISCOVERED THE SPRING
    by Raymond Macdonald Alden   176

WHY THE IVY IS ALWAYS GREEN *by Madge Bigham*   184

CANDLES AT MIDNIGHT *by Alice Geer Kelsey*   189

THE LOVELIEST ROSE IN THE WORLD
    by Hans Christian Andersen   198

BRINGING IN THE SPRING *by Elizabeth Yates*   202

CONTENTS

THE APPLE TREE *by Margery Williams Bianco* 209

THE SELFISH GIANT *by Oscar Wilde* 221

SECRETS AT THE MARDI GRAS
by Joan and Josephine Costantino 227

THE PASSION PLAY OF OBERAMMERGAU
by Janette Woolsey 239

THE LITTLE WHITE LILY: STORY OF THE EASTER SEAL
by Elizabeth Hough Sechrist 242

IT'S TIME FOR EASTER

THE EASTER STORY

The Easter Story as Told in the Gospels According to St. Matthew, St. Mark, St. Luke, and St. John

For God so loved the world, that he gave his only begotten Son, that whosoever believeth in him should not perish, but have everlasting life.

Then the soldiers of the governor took Jesus into the common hall, and gathered unto him the whole band of soldiers. And they stripped him and put on him a scarlet robe. And when they had platted a crown of thorns, they put it upon his head, and a reed in his right hand: and they bowed the knee before him, and mocked him, saying, Hail, King of the Jews! And after that they had mocked him, they took the robe off from him, and put his own raiment on him, and led him away to crucify him.

And when they had crucified him, they parted his garments, casting lots upon them, what every man should take.

And it was about the sixth hour, and there was a darkness over all the earth until the ninth hour. And the sun was darkened, and the veil of the temple was rent in the midst. And when Jesus

*had cried with a loud voice, he said, Father into thy hands I com-
mend my spirit: and having said thus, he gave up the ghost. Now
when the centurion saw what was done, he glorified God, saying,
Certainly this was a righteous man.*

*When the even was come, there came a rich man of Arimathaea,
named Joseph, who also himself was Jesus' disciple: He went to
Pilate, and begged the body of Jesus. Then Pilate commanded the
body to be delivered. And when Joseph had taken the body, he
wrapped it in a clean linen cloth, and laid it in his own new
tomb, which he had hewn out in the rock: and he rolled a great
stone to the door of the sepulchre, and departed.*

*And Mary Magdalene and Mary the mother of Joses beheld
where he was laid.*

*In the end of the sabbath, as it began to dawn toward the
first day of the week, came Mary Magdalene and the other Mary
to see the sepulchre. And, behold, there was a great earthquake:
for the angel of the Lord descended from heaven, and came and
rolled back the stone from the door, and sat upon it. His counte-
nance was like lightning, and his raiment white as snow: And
for fear of him the keepers did shake and became as dead men.
And the angel answered and said unto the women, Fear not ye:
for I know that ye seek Jesus which was crucified. He is not here;
for he is risen, as he said. Come, see the place where the Lord lay.
And go quickly, and tell his disciples that he is risen from the
dead; and, behold, he goeth before you into Galilee; there shall
ye see him: lo, I have told you. And they departed quickly from
the sepulchre with fear and great joy, and did run to bring his
disciples word. And as they went to tell his disciples, behold,
Jesus met them, saying, All hail. And they came and held him by
the feet, and worshipped him.*

THE HISTORY OF EASTER

In the earliest days of Christianity, Easter was celebrated at the same time as the Jewish Passover. There was a reason for this. The last days of Christ's life on earth were spent observing the Passover. He was crucified on Passover Day, which was the fourteenth day of the Jewish month Nisan. Christ rose from the dead on the following Sunday. Because of this, His followers began to observe Sunday as the Lord's Day instead of the Jewish Sabbath, Saturday.

Easter is the holiest of all Christian festivals. Let us see how it got its name. Christ's resurrection from the dead occurred in the Spring of the year. The word Easter was borrowed from the Teutonic festival of the Spring sun, Eastre. This was the season of new birth, an awakening in nature when all the earth sprang to new life. It was the death of Winter, the birth of Spring. The time of Christ's resurrection coincided with the revival of new life in nature. Thus the promise to mankind, of New Life through the risen Lord, has its counterpart in the Spring season of rebirth in nature with its green growing plants and flowers. We can understand why the symbols of Spring—the rising sun from the East, the flowers in their new bloom and trees in their new dress, new lambs in the fold--are so appropriate at Eastertide.

From the earliest years of the church, Easter was the favorite time for baptism. This, too, represented new life in its spiritual meaning as an awakening of the soul of the Christian into new life with Christ. Those who were baptized always wore white garments for the ceremony, and thus white became the color most closely associated with Easter.

In several European languages the name for Easter shows the influence of the Jewish Passover, Pesach. In Italian it is *Pasqua.* In Spanish it is *Pascua,* and in French, *Pâques.*

For more than two hundred years there was some disagreement about the day on which Easter should be celebrated. When Christ was on earth, the Jewish calendar was used by His people. This was reckoned by the lunar (moon) system. Because His death and resurrection came at the time of the Passover, its celebration later coincided with this festival on the fourteenth day of Nisan. The lunar calendar is a movable one, causing the Passover to fall at various times between March twenty-second and April twenty-second. For the most part, the Eastern Church kept the Passover date for Easter, while the Western Church celebrated it on the first Sunday after the fourteenth of Nisan.

Then came the Council of Nicea. In the year 325 A.D. in the time of the Emperor Constantine, the Council, with the help of the Archbishop of Alexandria and the astronomers of the day, decreed that Easter should fall on the first Sunday after the first full moon following the vernal equinox.

But this did not bring an end to the differences. At the time the date for Easter was determined by the Nicene Council, the Julian calendar was the one in use. But in the year 1582, the Gregorian (our present) calendar was introduced by Pope Gregory XIII. This calendar was accepted immediately by all Roman Catholic nations, but not by the countries of the Eastern Orthodox faith, and not by Great Britain. Great Britain and her colonies did not accept it until 1752. For nearly two hundred years, between the sixteenth and eighteenth centuries, Easter was observed by the various nations at different times according to their religious beliefs. When Great Britain and the American colonies accepted the Gregorian calendar, there was an eleven days' difference.

The majority of the Christian nations had finally accepted the New Style calendar. But a difference still existed, for the Eastern Church continued to observe the Julian calendar for its church festivals. When, after many years, the Gregorian calendar was adopted by the Eastern Orthodox Church it still used the Julian calendar in reckoning the date of Easter. That is why, to this day,

Easter of the Eastern Church usually falls thirteen days after the same festival in the Western Church.

Members of the Eastern Orthodox Church believe their church is older than the Roman Catholic Church because they say it began in the Holy Lands, before Christianity was taken to Rome. That is why they believe they are the first to have observed Easter.

From the earliest times in history the sun was the center of great interest in the celebration of Spring. For this was the time when the sun brought warmth and life to the earth and caused the plants to come to light after their winter's sleep. Spring festivals were celebrated by all races of peoples at the time of the vernal equinox. After the resurrection of Christ, this event was given new meaning when the risen Son of God became the center of the Easter festival. The people greeted the rising sun of Easter Day with joy.

Some of the ancient legends about the sun persisted through the centuries. One of these was the belief that the sun danced on Easter Day. To demonstrate it, a vessel of water was placed outdoors under the morning sun. As the air caused motions in the water, the sun was reflected in waves and seemed to be dancing.

Lights played an important role in the church celebrations of Easter Eve. After the darkness and despair of Good Friday and the solemn anticipation of Holy Saturday, the people were happy to share in the sudden illumination of Easter Eve. Homes, after having been kept darkened, were made bright with all the lights the house possessed, and every church was illuminated with hundreds of candles. People on the streets carried their lighted tapers. Christ was the Light of the World, and the arrival of the Resurrection Day was honored with every kind of light the people could produce. Fires were even kindled on the hilltops and could be seen burning for miles around. The people took brands from the fire and carried them home as a protection from fire and lightning.

Most representative of all was the great Paschal candle that was lit in every church. It is said that some of these weighed as much as three hundred pounds. After the candle had been lighted and the light blessed, the candles of those in the congregation were lit from the Paschal light and carried home. These lights were used only on special occasions.

From the time that Easter was first celebrated, Easter Eve was spent as a night of prayer. It was called the Easter Vigil. The churches were always crowded on that night, and those who could not get inside stood with the crowds outside the church. For those who were fortunate enough to get inside, the services were an unforgettable experience. There was the lighting of the large Paschal candle, and then at midnight the consecration of the waters of the baptismal font. Then followed the baptism of the men, women, and children, in that order. In those days, those who were baptized were anointed with holy oil. Then they donned

their white robes. The services lasted until dawn, for at that time the Easter Vigil lasted all night. The Blessing of the Font in the Roman Catholic Church in modern times takes place on the morning of Holy Saturday.

In years gone by, there was a belief that running water was sanctified at Easter time. It used to be the practice of the women and girls, in some country sections of Europe, to wash their faces in a running stream in the belief that it would endow them with health and beauty. It was the custom, too, for the boys to sprinkle the girls with perfumed water. In some countries, such as Poland and Hungary, this practice is still carried out on Easter Monday.

In the early history of the church, the Easter festival was celebrated for eight days. This was called the Easter Octave. In the year 1094 it was reduced to a three-day observance. Most people shunned all work during Holy Week and the courts were closed. The people went to church every day. In the time of the Roman Empire, slaves were often given their freedom at Easter. At a later period, in England, the poor of the parish were given a free meal in the church on Easter afternoon. One historian tells of an occasion when two hundred and seventy loaves of bread, a quantity of cheese, and six hundred cakes were doled out to the paupers who crowded the church.

In olden times, people greeted each other at the Easter service in the church with a kiss. In Poland on Easter Day, the people still accost each other with the greeting used for hundreds of years: "A joyful Alleluia to you!" Among the Greeks and Slavs, the greeting has always been: "Christ is risen!" with the response, "Truly, He is risen."

For several hundred years, before the adoption of the Gregorian calendar, the New Year fell on March twenty-fifth. Consequently, Easter sometimes fell at the beginning of the new year. It is said that even today, especially in France, an occasional "Happy New Year" is heard.

In the time of the Puritans, all holidays were frowned upon

as being too worldly. The celebration of Christmas had become so far different from the reverent observance it was intended to be that the Puritans of England finally made it unlawful to celebrate it at all. Then in 1643, the British Parliament struck Christmas, Easter, and Whitsuntide from the calendar.

When the Puritans came from English shores to settle in New England, they brought with them the customs and beliefs of the old country. Easter was ignored, even by the churches. It is hard to realize today that in the early history of our country Easter was celebrated hardly at all. The exceptions to this were the states of Louisiana and Maryland where Catholics had settled. Gradually, Easter became important again, and in the past fifty or sixty years Lent and Easter have been widely observed in the United States.

Easter in the United States today is filled with a wide variety of customs that have come from peoples all over the world, East and West. In these customs we can see the historical influence of this holy festival as it was kept by the people through the centuries. We know that many of the features of Easter, such as the name itself, the Eastre of the pagan festival of Springtime, are very, very old. Most of the church rites of Easter have come down to us through the ages from the early Christian Church. As the people have faithfully carried out their manner of celebrating this holiest of all holidays, Easter has become endeared to them with the years. The message of that first Easter morning when the angel of the Lord spoke from the empty tomb of Christ is still a message of hope and joy to all the world: *He is not here; for he is risen.*

EASTER CUSTOMS

The Days of Lent

Easter is a holy day which differs from all others because it is preceded by a preparation time of forty days. This time of preparation is known as Lent. The name is believed to have come from the word *Lengten-tid*, Anglo-Saxon for Springtime. *Lengten-tid* meant a "lengthening time" or a time when the days were growing longer. The period of Lent does not include Sundays. It begins on Ash Wednesday and ends with Holy Saturday.

Lent is a time of fasting, set aside by the Christian Church in memory of the forty days of fasting by Christ before His Crucifixion.

SHROVE TUESDAY

In years gone by it was the custom not only to give up meat during Lent but also to avoid all foods containing fats. Therefore the people, knowing that fats must not be eaten during Lent, tried to use up all that was left on Shrove Tuesday, the day before Lent was to begin.

Shrove Tuesday was a day set aside many, many years ago by the early Roman Church for everyone to go to church and confess his sins. The old English word for confess was shrive. The people who made confession were "shrove." Thus the day became known as Shrove Tuesday.

Shrove Tuesday in England was often called Pancake Day because it was the custom on that day to fry pancakes to use the cooking fat that was left. An early book on England tells of a pancake bell that was rung early in the morning on Shrove Tuesday to announce that it was time for all good cooks to begin frying pancakes. An old rhyme said:

> *But hark, I hear the pancake bell,*
> *And fritters make a gallant smell.*

Cakes in a variety of forms are popular in many European countries for Shrove Tuesday fare. The Norwegians make a rich cake filled with whipped cream called *bollers*. The Germans and Austrians eat rich crullers fried in fat. In German-speaking sections of Europe and the United States these are always eaten on Shrove Tuesday and are known as *fastnachts,* German for Fast Night. In Switzerland the *fastnachts* contain caraway seeds. In Finland, rich pancakes called *blini* are eaten with hot milk on this day, accompanied by a traditional pea soup. A soup made of pigs' feet is a Shrove Tuesday dish in the country of Estonia.

Children of Norway and Denmark have a most unusual way of celebrating the pre-Lenten season. Early on the morning of *Fastelavn,* they rush to their parents' bedroom and switch them with Lenten switches. For this they are rewarded with delicious Shrovetide buns. These buns, besides being eaten, are featured sometimes in a game similar to Bite-the-Apple. The bun is suspended from the ceiling on a string and the boys and girls, with their hands held behind them, try to take a bite from the swinging bun.

Shrove Tuesday is a school holiday for the boys and girls of Finland. The favorite sport there is coasting, and there is an old belief that the finer the coasting on Shrovetide the better the crops next harvest.

In France, the Tuesday before Lent is known as Mardi Gras, or Fat Tuesday. On that day in Paris, a huge ox is carried through the streets in a long procession consisting of the butchers of Paris. The Fat Ox is followed by the King of Butchers who, strangely enough, is a small boy. The car in which the boy rides is soon filled with flowers and sweets thrown into the passing car by the crowds of spectators.

Carnivals are popular before Lent in almost all European countries. They began many years ago when very strict fasts were kept during Lent by the people. Knowing that a forty-day fast lay ahead, everyone felt the urge, on the day before it was to start, to feast and make merry. The carnivals were always attended by crowds of people wearing masks and costumes. This custom is very old indeed, dating back to a holiday of ancient Rome. In a few countries, the carnivals of Shrovetide still keep some of the characteristics of the old Roman festival. In the Austrian Alps, a Dance of the Phantoms is held annually. For hundreds of years this strange dance, composed entirely of men, has depicted the struggle between Winter and Spring. In parts of Germany, where a similar performance takes place, an effigy of Winter is burned. Then Spring is welcomed into the village with joyous music and merrymaking.

In Frosinone, Italy, there is an interesting carnival held on Shrove Tuesday called *Radica*. The carnival gets its name from the fact that everyone carries a *radice* (root) of the agave plant in his hand. The highlight of the procession at this festival is an immense effigy of Carnival. Nine feet high, the effigy sits in a gaily bedecked cart drawn by four horses. By means of an arrangement of manipulated strings, the grotesque character waves its arms at the crowds. In some places where Carnival is represented by an image, it is seized by the crowds at the end of the procession and buried. This act represents the death of Winter.

The term Mardi Gras applies not only to the day of Shrove Tuesday, but also to the week preceding that day. On the Friday of Mardi Gras week in Ponti, Italy, a huge omelet is made from one thousand eggs. The omelet is later distributed to the poor along with other foods and wine.

In Rome, the beginning of the Mardi Gras procession is announced by young men dressed as monks.

Everywhere that the carnival is celebrated it features a merrymaking crowd of masked people dressed in costume. The Mardi Gras is of French origin. Brought to the United States by French settlers to New Orleans in the early 1700's, the New Orleans Mardi Gras is the most famous in this country. The festival is also observed in certain sections of Alabama, Florida, and Texas.

[34]

ASH WEDNESDAY

In Germany and Austria, the church bells peal out at midnight of Shrove Tuesday to herald the arrival of Ash Wednesday. For this is the true beginning of the Lenten season. Long years ago, at the beginning of the sixth century, Pope Gregory I set the time for the start of Lent as Ash Wednesday.

At the time of the early history of the Christian Church, the Lenten period was set aside as a time of penitence and fasting. The first day, Ash Wednesday, was held to be particularly solemn, when the people grieved over the magnitude of their sins. For thousands of years ashes were a symbol of penitence and mourning. It is believed that the custom of wearing ashes was borrowed from the Jewish religion.

Ash Wednesday gets its name from the ceremony performed in all Catholic churches of the Western World in which the mark of the cross is made with blessed ashes on the foreheads of church members. The ashes used in this ceremony have been saved from the previous year's palms of Palm Sunday. The palms are burnt and the ashes are blessed by the priest.

Ash Wednesday in Protestant churches is observed in various ways. In many churches Holy Communion is served on that day. For all church members it is a time of meditation and prayer.

In the countries of Austria, Germany, and Poland, there was always one food that made its appearance on Ash Wednesday. This was the pretzel. Pretzel is the German contraction for the Latin word meaning "little arms." This baked dough was made to take the place of bread, for it must be remembered that milk, eggs, and fats were forbidden during Lent. And so the pretzel, still very popular today as a food that can be eaten at any time of the year, was first created by bakers back in the fifth century A.D. The dough was made of flour, salt, and water and twisted in such a way as to represent two arms crossed in the act of prayer. When the pretzels were eaten they were remindful of the reverence associated with the season of Lent, and this for many years was the only time they were eaten. Pretzels were given to the paupers of the town in place of bread on certain days of Lent.

The practice of fasting during Lent gave rise to many curious customs. On Ash Wednesday in Spain, the people go through an ancient ritual called the Burial of the Sardine! A strip of pork or a sausage, representing the sardine, is buried amid much ceremony. The original purpose was to remind the people that meat would be gone from their lives for forty days and fish would take its place.

PALM SUNDAY

Palm Sunday is the Sunday before Easter. It commemorates the entry of Jesus into Jerusalem. The Gospels tell us: *When they heard that Jesus was coming to Jerusalem, [the people] took branches of palm trees, and went forth to meet him.*

Palm Sunday ushers in Holy Week. At the morning services on this day palms are given out to the congregation in Roman Catholic and Episcopal churches. In most European countries, the "palm" is a pussy-willow branch. That is why some nations call this day Willow Sunday. In churches of the Catholic faith, the *St. Matthew Passion* is sung during the Mass. In Protestant churches too, there is special music. A favorite composition heard in almost all Protestant churches is "The Palms" by Jean-Baptiste Faure.

In Italy, on Palm Sunday, there is a dramatization of the opening and closing of the gates of Jerusalem when Christ entered that city. After "the gates" of the church are opened, a procession of church officials, carrying palms, marches from the portico of the church to the altar where Mass is said.

In Mexico, the palms that have been blessed and given to the congregation are fashioned in the shape of a cross. This cross is fastened to the balcony of the house to keep it safe for the coming year.

In Slavic countries and in Austria, farmers and their families carry the blessed palms or willows in a procession through the fields. As they visit each field they chant hymns and leave a bit of the palm; the barns and other farm buildings are visited in the same way. This is done to bring the blessing of God upon the animals and crops.

Children of Finland decorate their willow branches with gay paper flowers. Then they put them away for Easter Sunday, when it is the custom to switch their friends with them! Those who get switched must pay a forfeit of Easter eggs.

On the eve of Palm Sunday in Yugoslavia, it is the custom for a young girl to place the blossoms of some flowers in a basin of water. On Palm Sunday morning, when she rises, she washes her face in the water in the belief that it will make her beautiful.

HOLY THURSDAY

This day is often called Maundy Thursday. The word Maundy is believed by some to come from the old French verb *maundier*, to beg. They reason that it was so called because of the beggars whose feet were washed on this day according to custom. However, Maundy may have come from the word "mandate." For Thursday was the mandate or order of Jesus, who washed the feet of His disciples and commanded them to do likewise. Jesus said, *If I then, your Lord and Master, have washed your feet, ye also ought to wash one another's feet.*

In England, years ago, it was the habit of the ruler of that nation to wash the feet of as many paupers as his age and to present them with gifts of money and new shoes. When Queen Elizabeth I was thirty-nine years old she washed the feet of thirty-nine paupers. The custom today in the Church of England is to present silver coins to as many persons as correspond in number to the reigning monarch's years of age.

In Armenia, Syria, and other Eastern countries, a foot-washing ceremony takes place in the church on Maundy Thursday.

In the Ukraine, it is believed to be beneficial to bathe in the river on Holy Thursday, for on that day the waters are said to have curative powers.

On Holy Thursday in Holland, boys and girls go from door to door singing an old song, begging for Easter eggs. As they sing they wave long sticks decorated with green garlands. In this way they collect enough eggs to take part in the egg games of Easter Monday.

In Hungary, where the day is known as "Green Thursday," it is customary to eat a green vegetable, usually spinach, for supper. The Germans eat a green salad on this day to keep from becoming "a donkey." It is also considered good luck in Germany to carry a green-colored egg in the pocket on Maundy Thursday.

[39]

In most European countries there is a saying that the church bells, which are always silent through Thursday to Saturday, fly to Rome to spend Good Friday with the Pope at the Vatican. In Austria, where even the bells of the clocks are kept silent, the hour is announced by boys who go about the town with wooden clappers. Each hour they sing a different stanza of a song which tells the events of Christ's Passion.

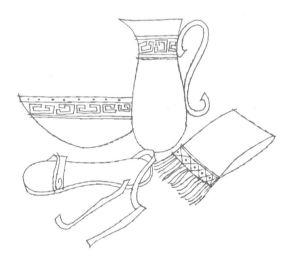

GOOD FRIDAY

Good Friday is the most solemn of all religious holy days. It commemorates the Crucifixion of our Lord. All over the Christian world on that day church services are held from noon until three o'clock, the hours when Christ suffered on the Cross. The day is one of sadness and prayer and fasting for many millions of Christians. The Germans call it the "Friday of Mourning." Beautiful musical compositions have been written for Good Friday by the great composers of the world. Probably the greatest of these are the Bach *St. John Passion* and *St. Matthew Passion.* Bach choirs throughout the United States perform these annually.

One of the oldest ceremonies performed on Good Friday is the church ritual of the shrine of the Holy Sepulchre. A procession is formed and the Blessed Sacrament is carried to a small tabernacle called the Holy Sepulchre. The shrines of the Holy Sepulchre of various churches are visited by the faithful on Good Friday and Holy Saturday. Processions take place not only in the churches but also in the streets, and some of these are very impressive indeed. In Spain, Mexico, and most South American countries, the processions last for several days during Holy Week. In Spain they start on the Wednesday after Palm Sunday. *Pasos,* the figures representing the characters of the Passion, are mounted on platforms and carried by members of different organizations in the procession. All the scenes of the last week of Christ's life are represented. The figures are always dressed in costly garments and adorned with precious jewels. Some of the jewels are gifts to the organization presenting the *Pasos,* but some are loaned for the occasion. These processions in the large cities attract thousands of spectators, and people travel many miles to see them.

In Italy, boys carrying candles and figures representing the Angel of the Tomb, and other characters in the burial scene, follow the bier in which lies the figure of the Christ. This procession ends at the church where a service called *L'Agonia* is held.

Greek church members everywhere customarily take part in a funeral march through the streets. A flower-decked bier called an *epitaphios* containing a figure of the dead Christ is carried on the shoulders of four men. A long procession follows it, wending its way toward the church. At the church service, the candles and flowers that have been carried in the procession are blessed by the priest and given out to those attending the service. The *Epitaphios* of Athens, Greece, on Good Friday is famous for its pageantry and dignity.

In the small country of Monaco there is a famous procession on Good Friday called *Christ Mort*. It has been held for centuries and consists of the characters of the Passion Week as well as long lines of members of the clergy and religious orders.

There are many traditional beliefs concerning Good Friday among the peoples of the world. Some farmers consider it the best day of the year to sow the fields, for it was on that day that Christ was laid in the earth. The farmers of Bulgaria believe if they sprinkle ashes around the chicken yards on Good Friday the eggs will be plentiful all year. An English superstition stated that if a woman washed her laundry on Good Friday the clothing would be spotted with blood. In Czechoslovakia after the Good Friday service is over, the people in the church run through the aisles "to chase out Judas."

In many countries all the bells are silent on Good Friday, and in Czechoslavakia and Yugoslavia people knock boards together to take the place of the sound of bells pealing.

A strange custom of a village in Sussex, England, was to play a game of marbles on Good Friday. Not only the boys but grown men played this game on the road leading to church and again after the services were over.

An observance of Good Friday that has lasted through the years is the custom of eating hot cross buns. These buns, with a cross marked on the top crust, are never eaten anywhere in the world except during Lent. Originally they were made to be eaten on Good Friday only. In those days they were made in the form of an unleavened bread. Gradually they became the sweet raised bun we know today with raisins in the batter and frosting on the top.

There was an old English rhyme that said:

> *One-a-penny buns,*
> *Two-a-penny buns,*
> *One-a-penny, two-a-penny*
> *Hot cross buns!*

Years ago the bakers and pastry chefs of English towns and villages vied with one another in making hot cross buns. In Chelsea, there were two royal bun houses where customers started lining up before six o'clock in the morning on Good Friday to buy the delicious buns. There were many superstitions connected with this Good Friday food. Some believed if the buns were ground up and water added they were good medicine for the ills of man and beast. People believed that eating the buns on Good Friday would bring good luck. There was an odd superstition that hot cross buns would never grow mouldy regardless of how long they were kept. An old book called *Poor Robin's Almanack* tells us:

> *Good Friday comes this month, the old woman runs*
> *With one- or two-a-penny hot cross buns,*
> *Whose virtue is, if you believe what's said,*
> *They'll not grow mouldy like the common bread.*

HOLY SATURDAY

Saturday of Holy Week has always been a rather quiet time, for it was on this day that Christ rested in the Tomb. It is a time of waiting for the Resurrection of Easter Morn. However, there are some rites and customs connected with the day and especially the evening. The eve of Easter has been called the "Night of Illumination." From early times it was customary to light the Paschal candles on this night. From the large Paschal candle in the church, the people of the congregation lighted their individual Easter candles, then carried them home to light the home fires. The dark night of Easter Eve would be brightened with the sight of the many lights being carried home from church. There was the belief that the fire obtained from the blessed Paschal candle was a protection from lightning.

In Rumania, the young people are careful not to let their candle burn out before they reach home. When they arrive home, they use the light to gaze into a mirror to try to see what the future holds for them.

In Germany, it was long the custom to light fires on the hillside on the night of Holy Saturday. When the fire was burning brightly, the young people gathered around it to sing Easter hymns. Boys with flaming bundles of straw would run through the fields with them. This was to ensure good crops at the next harvest. In Austria, torches are lighted from the burning bonfires and a procession of musicians and singers wends its way through the streets of the village singing ancient Easter hymns.

In addition to the blessing of the lights, it was an ancient custom to bless the waters on Easter Eve. This ritual is preserved in modern times with the blessing of the Font that takes place in Catholic churches in the morning on Holy Saturday. The water, after it is blessed, is taken home in bottles by the faithful.

In certain places in Europe, the ponds, lakes, and streams of the locality are blessed by the priest.

In Bulgaria and Hungary, on Holy Saturday, the special eggs and cakes that have been prepared for Easter are taken to the church and blessed by the priest. In Italy, the homes and shops of a village are sprinkled with holy water and blessed by the priest.

In Czechoslovakia, they say that if it rains on Holy Saturday it will rain often during the coming year.

On Easter Eve in Holland, the young people of the town form a procession to the market square. They carry lighted candles and sing Easter hymns. When they have congregated, they have a social time with music and dancing.

In Poland, the food prepared for Easter, known as the hallow fare, is blessed on Holy Saturday by the priest when he visits the homes to perform this ceremony.

In most European countries, Holy Saturday is a busy day in the homes where Easter food is being prepared. In fact, Christians throughout the world are astir early on this day, preparing for the morrow! Special cakes are baked, Easter eggs are colored, the ham is cooked, and new clothes are made ready to be worn on the festive and glorious Easter Day. A time of rejoicing is at hand, and all who prepare for it await the day with gladness.

EASTER AROUND THE WORLD

IN THE EAST

We have seen, in our chapter on the history of Easter, how the celebration of this great church festival began in the Holy Lands of the Middle East. In these countries, where the Eastern Orthodox Church had its beginning and still predominates today, Easter is the holiest of all the holidays. Among these people Holy Week is known as the Week of Salvation, and Easter is called the Pasch of Resurrection.

In Jerusalem, on Maundy Thursday, there is always a public foot-washing ceremony. The Patriarchs (Heads) of the Church and twelve bishops, taking the part of the twelve disciples, re-enact the scene in the Gospels where Jesus washed the feet of His disciples.

In Armenia, the day after Easter is celebrated as the Feast of the Dead. Food is taken to the cemetery and there it is blessed by the priest, who also offers up prayers for the dead.

In many of the Eastern churches the priests keep a very strict diet during Lent, fasting for two days and eating only on the third day. Since the ancient time of the Council of Nicea in the year 325 A.D., it has been the custom for Eastern Orthodox Church members to say the Angelus on Easter in a standing position, thereby showing that the Christian is "risen" with Christ.

[46]

IN EUROPE

Easter in the British Isles is observed today in much the same manner as it is here in the United States. But in years gone by there were many quaint Easter customs among the people. For hundreds of years in England, for instance, twelve old women of Suffolk were chosen to play ball on Easter Monday; no one know why. Another old custom called "lifting" was carried out on the two days following Easter. On Easter Monday the men lifted their maiden friends and neighbors in a chair lined in white and gaily decorated with ribbons. On the following day the ladies lifted the gentlemen in the same way. This custom was said to be "a memorial of Christ being raised up from the grave." In some towns on Easter Sunday it was customary for the children to "clip" or embrace the church. Dressed in their best clothes, a ring of boys and girls joined hands and formed a complete circle around the church, with their backs to the building. Then they formed a procession to the next church, where the ceremony was repeated. The origin of many of the Easter customs carried out so faithfully by the people has long since been forgotten.

It was considered bad luck to appear on Easter Sunday in anything other than new clothes, for the rhyme of the times said,

> *At Easter let your clothes be new*
> *Or else be sure you will it rue!*

The custom of wearing new clothes on Easter began in the earliest Christian time, when the people dressed in new white gowns for their baptismal ceremony.

In Scotland, a game of ball was played on Easter Monday with hard-boiled eggs instead of balls. In Ireland, on Easter Day, a dance contest was held in many places with young and old alike

entering into the fun. The prize was a special cake, and the phrase "He takes the cake" may well have started at that time.

In France, on Easter Sunday, the churches are crowded with the devout attending Mass. Later the streets are thronged with people dressed in their best, exchanging greetings, *"Heureuses Pâques!"* (Happy Easter!) Occasionally, too, one may hear the strange greeting, "Happy New Year!" This is an ancient carry-over from the time hundreds of years ago when Easter, by the old calendar, sometimes fell on the same day as the New Year.

In many Belgian churches, a foot-washing ceremony is held on Holy Thursday for twelve men who have been selected from the town's almshouse. After the ceremony, the men are presented with gifts. On Easter morning the children of Belgium rush out to the garden to find the eggs hidden in the leaves and shrubbery. And how did they get there? The bells of the churches have dropped them in the garden, the children are told.

German children have a game that is traditionally played on the Saturday night before Easter. They roll eggs on tracks made of sticks. On Easter night, huge festival fires are lit on Germany's hilltops. In Lügde, the young people take large wheels and stuff them with straw. Then they set fire to the dry straw and roll the wheels, ablaze with flying fire, down the hillside.

Easter in Switzerland is celebrated according to the area. Where the French- or Italian-speaking people live, the day is observed by Roman Catholics purely as a religious festival. In the German sections where most of the people are Protestants, German customs prevail. In all the towns and cities of Switzerland, however, the people dress in their best clothes on this day which seems to usher in Spring, a season eagerly looked forward to after the long cold winter.

In Italy, a visitor to the house never refuses the Easter eggs offered from the huge pile of them that have been blessed by the priest for this event. On Holy Saturday in Florence, a unique custom is always observed. It dates from the time of the Crusades.

On that day, two white oxen may be seen on the streets of Florence, drawing a beautiful flower-bedecked cart filled with fireworks. The cart finally stops before the door of the great cathedral and a strange operation takes place. Wires are strung from the cart to the altar inside the cathedral. When all is ready and the crowds stand tensely watching, an artificial bird called a firebird suddenly speeds along the wire from inside the church. When it touches the cart, fireworks are ignited and immediately the little bird or "dove" dashes back and disappears within the church. If it can time its return to the altar to beat the explosion of the cart, all is well. The people watch breathlessly, for the belief is that if the trip isn't timed just right, the crops of the following year will suffer. Fortunately for the farmers and all who eat the good Italian food, the little bird usually flies home in time.

On Easter Day in Greece, a special bread is eaten called the Bread of Christ. A Greek cross to represent the Crucifixion is always marked in its top crust, and the bread loaf is decorated with Easter eggs. On Easter Monday, in this country, traditional folk dances are performed.

In Albania, an Easter dinner always includes unleavened bread and roast lamb. Guests to the house on Easter Day are presented with two colored eggs.

Russia has a special Easter cake marked on top with the sign XB, meaning "Christ is risen." In the Russian Orthodox Church in olden times, there was no day in the calendar so special as Easter. Many of the great cathedrals and churches of old Russia are today, in the Soviet Union, only museums. But in those places where members of the Orthodox Church still worship, Easter is devoutly celebrated as in years gone by.

In the Ukraine, there is music and dancing at Easter time when the young girls sing and dance to the traditional *Hahilki* music. The Ukrainians extend the observance of Easter to two weeks. Holy Week is a time of reverence, but the week following Easter is spent in a social way with visiting and parties.

In Czechoslovakia, Easter Monday is a day reserved for sports events. In Latvia, it is customary to exchange small gifts on Easter Sunday. In this country and in Rumania, swings are set up in the form of platforms in the village square. A young maiden and her swain stand facing each other, and the swing is pushed by the other young people so high that it looks as though the couple would topple off. But the higher they go the better the young people like it. Hundreds of years ago, when this custom began, it was called "Swinging in the Spring," or, ushering in the Spring season.

Easter Monday is a day of fun for the boys and girls of Hungary. The boys sprinkle perfumed water on the girls, who reward this mischief by serving the boys a meal of hot bread and wine and Easter eggs!

In Spain, no bells are rung from Holy Thursday until Saturday. In this music-loving land there is dancing on Easter Sunday. In all the larger cities there are bullfights held in the afternoon, attended by thousands of people enjoying their favorite national sport.

In Norway, Easter is known as *påske*. An egg game is very popular in Norway. It is played by rolling hard-boiled eggs down a slope. The eggs hit against each other until one, which remains uncracked to the last, is declared the winner. Winter sports are enjoyed on Easter Day in the mountains of Norway and Sweden. But first an outdoor service is held to remind the people of the true meaning of the holiday. In Sweden, the festivities of Easter extend through Monday, or the Second Day of Easter as it is called. In Norway, the holidays last from Holy Thursday to Easter Tuesday. In Finland, a traditional Easter cake is eaten. It contains rye meal and is baked in birch baskets.

IN SOUTH AMERICA

In South American cities, the Lent of Easter is preceded by a great frolic known as Carnival. This takes place on Shrove Tuesday and is celebrated with immense parades, band music, dancing, and so much hilarity that the police are kept busy trying to maintain law and order. However, once Lent has begun all the traditions of the Church are devoutly adhered to by the people, especially during Passion Week. On Palm Sunday, known there as Flower Sunday, people place the palms they have brought home from church behind their doors. This is to assure them of good luck and peace to the household throughout the coming year. On Holy Thursday a Last Supper is re-enacted in the church. On Good Friday, at three o'clock in the afternoon, the priest removes the Christ from the Cross which has been erected in the *monumento* on the day before. It is placed solemnly in the Sepulchre and is visited by worshipers the rest of the day and evening. *Pascua,* Easter Sunday, is the most important religious day of the year.

IN MEXICO

In Mexico, the observance of the Easter season is similar to that of South American countries. But in Mexico the children take an active part in the celebration. In some sections on Holy Thursday, the children carry rattles to "drive out the devils" by making as much noise as they possibly can, and you may be sure they all enjoy this. On Holy Saturday, at noon, there is even more excitement on the streets of Mexican towns when the Judases are punished. Grownups as well as children take part when effigies of Judas, all of them very ugly and forbidding, are publicly beaten and sometimes hanged or burned. This is a reminder of the Biblical character Judas Iscariot, the betrayer of Christ. Sometimes, especially in the homes, the Judas turns out to be nothing more than a *piñata* (pot) filled with sweets. When soundly beaten with a stick the pot breaks and scatters goodies at the children's feet. All this fun, on Saturday, follows the solemn day of Good Friday when no such gaiety is thought of. On that day a sober funeral procession wends its way through the streets to the church. Sometimes a passion play is enacted outside the church door. Easter Day itself is a glorious day of rejoicing, with Mass and beautiful music in the churches. The afternoon is spent, as in Spain, with thousands of people attending the bullfights.

IN THE U.S.A.

A day that heralds Easter in the United States, though it seems far removed from it, is Shrove Tuesday, the day before Lent begins. The most notable celebration of this day is the carnival of several Southern cities. Most famous is the Mardi Gras Carnival of New Orleans. Mardi Gras officially begins in that city with a ball that is held on Twelfth Night after Christmas. But the grand parade and the most important ball are held on Mardi Gras Day, Shrove Tuesday. A king, a queen, and their court are all chosen to head the social events of the Mardi Gras. People from places all over the United States and even from South and Central America crowd into the city to see the carnival. When the parade passes, there are often twenty or more spectacular floats of almost indescribable splendor. These are accompanied by many bands of musicians and hundreds of people all dressed in splendid costumes, wending their way through the streets. Most of the half million or so spectators play their parts in the colorful scene by wearing fancy costumes. All are masked. After the parade is over, people make their way to a Grand Ball where a king, a queen, and their court preside over the festivities. Dancing lasts until midnight. Mardi Gras in New Orleans has been observed, with very few exceptions, since 1766.

A far different celebration of Shrove Tuesday is noted by the German settlers of Pennsylvania. Among the older citizens of Pennsylvania German localities, the day is known as *Fassnacht*. *Fassnacht* is Pennsylvania Dutch for Fast Night. Delicious crullers called fassnachts are traditionally fried and eaten on this day. If some are left over they may be eaten for breakfast the following morning. The custom of eating fassnachts came over to America more than two hundred years ago with settlers from the Palatinate. When the dough is fried on Shrove Tuesday morning, the last small piece of it is dropped into the hot fat and when it is done

is presented to *die Fassnacht,* the lazy member of the family who is last to come down to breakfast.

The dawn of an Easter Day in the United States is greeted by millions of men, women, and children all over the land attending sunrise services. In cemeteries flower-decked for the glad anniversary of the Resurrection, in athletic fields, on fair grounds, and on hilltops of hundreds of towns, the people throng to services where they greet the dawn singing praises to the risen Lord. Almost every town and village and city takes part in this beautiful custom. One of the first of these to be held in our country was in Bethlehem, Pennsylvania, many years ago. The custom has never faltered, and to the present time, about three o'clock on the morning of Easter, a sound of trombones rings through the air, calling the people of Bethlehem to worship. While the world is still dark the people throng into the old Moravian Burying Ground close by the church to await the rising sun of a new Easter Day. And as the sun appears, thousands of voices, to the accompaniment of the Trombone Choir, greet it with a ringing song of praise: *Christ is risen!*

In America's fiftieth state of Hawaii, glorious Easter sunrise services are held annually at the Punchbowl, a passive volcanic crater overlooking the city of Honolulu.

Music presented in American churches for the Easter season usually follows a certain pattern. On Good Friday a church choir, often with special soloists taking part, will present such works as Bach's *St. Matthew Passion* or his equally beautiful *St. John Passion,* or perhaps *The Seven Last Words* by Joseph Haydn. On Easter morning in Roman Catholic churches, the Easter Mass is sung with great beauty and reverence. The Easter music that swells through the air in churches all over the nation expresses praise and happiness. An old English hymn describes the quality of the music of Easter in these words:

Come, ye faithful, raise the strain of triumphant gladness!

And in thousands of churches on Easter morning millions of voices sing the old familiar lines of the hymn by Charles Wesley:

Christ the Lord is risen today, Alleluia!

On Sunday afternoon, an annual Easter parade occurs in towns and cities from one end of the country to the other when people walk out in their new "Easter best." Most famous of the Easter parades are those in New York City on Fifth Avenue and on the Boardwalk of Atlantic City. New clothes herald the Spring. With Spring the world comes to new life again. Christ is risen and there is joy and gladness everywhere!

Early on Easter morning, thousands of small boys and girls scramble out of bed in a hurry to see what the Easter rabbit has brought them. And what do many of them find? A gay wicker basket, with colored straw forming a nest, and the nest piled so high that the basket is fairly bursting with Easter eggs and chocolate rabbits and little marshmallow chicks! The Easter eggs vary, from the huge chocolate cream egg with the child's name written on it in white or pink icing, all decorated with fancy pink and green and white rosettes, to the colored hens' eggs and luscious fruit and nut eggs and marshmallow eggs of every hue, and the bittersweet chocolate ones that are hollow inside, down to the very tiny gelatin eggs known as jelly beans, every color of the rainbow, dripping down through the straw! Sometimes, too, there's an old-fashioned egg that may have belonged to Grandma. This is the most interesting egg of all. It's made of frosted glass, hollow inside and containing a little round window through which, if you squint one eye, you can see a miniature garden of flowers with perhaps some bluebirds flying above.

No wonder the children hasten to see what the Easter bunny has brought them! The Easter basket holds almost as much pleasure for them as the Christmas stocking. But why are there all these Easter eggs and chocolate bunnies at Easter, and why are the children told that the Easter bunny has brought them? There *is* a reason.

First of all, let us take the case of the Easter rabbit. The rabbit is also called a hare. According to Egyptian mythology, the hare is a symbol of the moon. It is thought that its significance at

Easter is its association with the date of the festival, for that date is determined by the moon. When the Christian fathers met at the Council of Nicea back in the year 325, the date of Easter was definitely settled and has been kept by their ruling ever since. It was decided that Easter should be kept upon the first Sunday after the first *full moon* following the twenty-first day of March. And so the hare, representing the moon, came to be associated with the Easter festival.

For hundreds of years in certain sections of England, hare hunts have been held on Easter. An ancient custom in the county of Warwick had to do with the Easter hare. If this little animal could be caught and taken to the village parson before ten o'clock on Easter morning, the parson, in return, was obliged to give the young people who caught it a hundred eggs for breakfast!

In Germany, Switzerland, and Belgium, the boys and girls put nests in the grass in their gardens so that the Easter rabbit may fill them with eggs. But if the weather turns out to be unpleasant, the rabbit finds places inside the house to hide the eggs. In Italy, bunny-shaped pastries are baked for the Easter feast.

As for the Easter eggs! They are so closely related to the festival all over the Christian world that Easter would not seem right without them. Even before the time of Christ it was customary to exchange eggs. The Hebrews, for hundreds of years, have included the Paschal egg at the feast of the Passover. The ancient peoples of Egypt, Persia, Greece, and Rome followed the custom of exchanging eggs at their Spring festivals. In Babylonia, eggs were presented to the ancient goddess of fertility, Astarte. A very old Hindu myth told how the world itself was created from a giant world-egg. After the mammoth egg had lain dormant for a period of time, the story went, it finally split into two halves, the earth and the sky. To people of all ages, the egg has represented new life. What more appropriate sign of the Resurrection, then, than that it should signify the new birth in the risen Lord! And so Christian people have welcomed it at the celebration of Easter.

In Ireland the fast of Lent is broken at dawn on Easter day by eating a meal of eggs.

It is the custom in some parts of France for the children to take gifts of eggs to the priest when they go to church on Holy Saturday to make confession. In that country, in days gone by, egg races were held at the Easter fetes. The prize for the winner was a hogshead of cider! All over Europe, egg races are popular at Easter time. The eggs are saved carefully by the children throughout Holy Week.

English children are presented with gifts of chocolate eggs wrapped in fancy colored paper. In Austrian or German families, presents are often given to the children concealed within an imitation Easter egg. The little egg-shaped boxes are saved and used all year to hold trinkets. In Germany it is thought to bring good luck to carry a green-colored egg on the person on Maundy Thursday.

Through the years many methods of coloring eggs were used by the country people to whom commercial dyes were not available. They made use of onion skins, herb juices, furze (a shrub with yellow flowers), various species of flowers, and bits of colored cloth soaked in hot water to bring out the dye color.

In the Tyrol the children collect eggs on Easter Eve. They go about from farmhouse to farmhouse, singing carols. They carry baskets with them, and into the baskets go the gifts of Easter eggs from the farmers' wives as reward for their songs. The eggs have been specially prepared for the children, all dyed in bright colors and decorated. Some of them have religious mottoes printed on them.

In England long ago, messages were often written on the eggs that were sent to friends and relatives. It sometimes happened that years later these eggs, if the date had appeared on them, were used for proof in establishing facts in family records.

Italian families bake a special round cake for the holy day which they decorate with Easter eggs. The Italians take their

eggs to church on Easter Eve, where they are blessed by the priest. At the Easter feast next day, these eggs are given the center of the table with everything else arranged around them. What a lot of them there are, sometimes as many as two hundred, all of them colored in gayest colors! There are so many because everyone who enters the house during the holidays is offered at least one egg, and no one may refuse this token of the Resurrection. The custom of paying calls on the afternoon of Easter Sunday is very popular in Southern Europe. Children look forward to it because at each place they are given Easter eggs and sweets.

In Czechoslovakia, eggs are given to pay a forfeit. On Easter Monday the boys make fancy, decorated willow whips and switch the girls with them! This is supposed to bring good luck to the girls, so they reward the boys with gaily decorated eggs.

In Yugoslavia and in other places where the Slavic people live, it is the custom to prepare great quantities of eggs on Great Thursday. Some of the eggs are dyed black and these are placed on the graves of departed members of the family. In Greece and Rumania the eggs are colored red to express the joy of the Easter season. When friends meet on Easter day, each knocks a red egg against the egg of the other person and the greeting, "Christ is risen!" is exchanged with the reply, "Truly, He is risen."

Red eggs are popular in the Ukraine, too. Young girls rub their cheeks with them on Easter for a rosy appearance. Nowhere else in the world, probably, are there such beautiful Easter eggs as in the villages of the Ukraine. For generations the villagers have made up their own designs, using homemade tools and dyes for the intricate work. The designs feature chapels, belfries, priests' robes, fir trees, and other interesting subjects. The eggs, along with other Easter foods, are blessed by the priest on the eve of Easter, then taken home for the feast on the morrow. The Ukrainians cast the shells of some of their eggs upon the waters in honor of the dead.

Bulgarian families, who prefer red Easter eggs, always place

the first decorated egg before the family icon as a symbol of the Resurrection.

Empty eggshells are used in several European countries for decoration and display on Easter Day. The uncooked egg is pierced with a needle at each end and the contents of the egg are blown out. Easter egg trees made of these hollow eggshells are especially popular in Germany. The decorated shells are suspended from a branch or from a small tree. Then the Easter egg tree is placed on a table in a prominent place where it is admired by visitors to the house. In Norway, the children use empty eggshells to make tiny baskets for holding small candies. Sometimes these are pasted shut after they are filled and are then hidden in nests to be found on Easter morning.

Easter egg trees have become popular in our own country, too. These and other Easter traditions have come to us from lands across the seas. One such custom came from Germany and Norway. It is the egg-rolling party that is given annually on Easter Monday on the lawn of the White House in the nation's capital. The wife of the President of the United States is the hostess. The party is attended by hundreds of eager children, each carrying a basket of colored eggs for the rolling. In all the running and tumbling and happy shouting that follow, no one stops to realize that this is a sport that has been popular for many, many years.

Egg rolling, Easter egg trees, nests of eggs hidden in the garden, Easter baskets found early on Easter morning—all these have a truly important place in the Easter celebration. Boys and girls have been enjoying them for hundreds of years in the past. Let us hope they will stay with us for many years to come!

EASTER LEGENDS

Symbols and Legends

Back in the early history of mankind there were certain natural facts which were puzzling to men. Because it is normal to want to understand what is happening, many beliefs which were attempts at explanation grew up among the people. And as these beliefs were passed down from generation to generation they became known as myths, or legends. Today, as we read these legends, it helps us to understand ancient peoples far better than we could if we didn't have them. For the legends represent their hopes and fears.

Closely associated with myths and legends is symbolism. Sometimes an object becomes a symbol for a quality that a person possesses. We say, "He is as brave as a lion." And the lion becomes a symbol of bravery.

Just so, down through the history of the church we have many legends and symbols. Sometimes the legends and symbols have their bases in facts. And sometimes the symbols take their meanings from the legends. Easter has acquired many symbols. Some originated from the Easter story itself. And some of those which are based on legends are found pictured in the paintings of the old masters. For example, a certain kind of flower does not get painted in a portrayal of the Crucified Christ just by chance. Rather it has a distinct purpose for being there. For all these things have meanings. They may be symbols to express emotions or, again, they may be reminders of well-known sacred legends. Here are some of the symbols and legends of Easter.

[71]

THE CROSS

The symbol of Christ's Crucifixion is the Cross. It signifies that Christ died for mankind and that no sacrifice He could make was too great. Besides this the Cross has come to mean the trials, whether they be large or small, that people have to endure. Sometimes when a person has a physical handicap it may be said, "It is the Cross he has to bear." Or, speaking of someone who gladly sacrifices his own comfort to give happiness to others, we say, "He bears his Cross with courage."

THE TOMB

The symbol of Christ's resurrection is the Tomb. Usually in paintings it is shown with the stone at one side rolled away from the opening and an angel guarding the entrance. It portrays for us the true meaning of Easter and explains why its story has such importance to all Christians. For as the Cross is the symbol of the suffering and the death of Christ, the empty Tomb symbolizes the Risen Lord and all the joy with which Easter Day is celebrated.

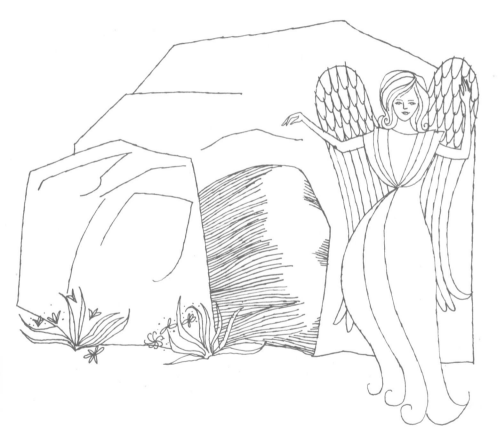

THE ASS

If you have ever seen a little Castilian donkey, or ass, you will notice that he is wearing a Cross on his back. There is a dark patch of hair which goes the length of his back and another which crosses his shoulders. The reason for this, says the legend, is that a colt of the ass was the animal Christ chose to ride when he made his triumphal entry into Jerusalem. The ass, therefore, will always bear the symbol of the Crucifixion of our Lord.

THE LION

A legend which ancient peoples believed was that lion cubs were born dead. After the cubs were three days old, it was thought that the lioness breathed on them and brought them to life. So the lion became a symbol of Easter, signifying that Christ lay dead for three days in the Tomb and then lived again.

THE WHALE

The whale, too, is an Easter symbol. Many persons thought that the story of Jonah was a prophecy of what would happen to Christ. In the Old Testament it is told that for three days Jonah lay in the belly of a great fish and then was cast up on dry land. Just so, Jesus lay dead for three days in the Tomb and then rose and came forth again into the light of the world.

THE RABBIT

The little rabbit is a very shy animal. And he has no weapons with which to defend himself, as do many other animals. Because of this frailness he is dependent on the goodness of others for his life. Therefore he is a symbol of Easter because he represents man, who has placed his hope in Christ who died to save him.

THE PHOENIX

There is a very curious legend about the phoenix. The phoenix was a mythological bird. According to the beliefs of ancient people, this bird lived for three hundred to five hundred years. But this wasn't the only remarkable thing about it. Every so often it would cast itself on a funeral pyre and be consumed in the flames. Then it would arise from its own ashes and begin life all over again. Because of these remarkable powers which had been attributed to it in the legend, some early Christians adopted it as a symbol of the Resurrection. They thought it signified that one can die as the phoenix did and be born again. For Christ died on the Cross and in three days was resurrected from the dead.

THE EAGLE

Closely related to the legend of the phoenix is the belief that the eagle, too, has very remarkable qualities. It was thought that the eagle restored its life by flying so close to the sun that its feathers were scorched and burned. While they were still burning, the eagle would plunge downward into water and miraculously its plumage would be restored. So the eagle, for the same reason as the phoenix, symbolized the rebirth of mankind through the Crucifixion and Resurrection of our Lord.

[79]

THE OWL

The owl is a strange bird that prefers darkness to light. Sometimes he is used as an Easter symbol and is seen in pictures showing the Crucifixion of Christ. This is because he is an example of people who also are in darkness. But Christ is the symbol of light for all people who truly believe in Him.

THE ROBIN

A lovely legend tells how the robin got his red breast. On the way to Calvary, a little robin noted that a thorn had pierced the forehead of Christ, causing it to bleed. So he flew down and plucked out the thorn. But as he did so, a drop of Christ's blood fell on the little bird's breast, staining it red. From that time forth, all robins have had red breasts as a reminder that one of them was kind to our Lord.

THE SWALLOW

On the day on which Christ was crucified, a little bird flew near the Cross on Calvary. The little bird, according to an old Scandinavian legend, felt sorry for our Lord and wished to help Him. So he called to Him, "Svale! Svale!" which means "Cheer up! Cheer up!" From that time forth, the little brown bird became known as the "Bird of Consolation" or "Swallow." And they believed something else about the little bird, too. They thought because he wasn't seen all winter that he hibernated in the mud. But when he emerged in the Springtime it was like a new birth or Resurrection.

THE BUTTERFLY

The butterfly is one of the symbols most often used to signify Easter. Its whole life cycle is symbolic of the meaning of Christianity. First there is the caterpillar, which stands for life. The second stage is the cocoon, which signifies death. And the third stage is the butterfly which emerges from the cocoon, portraying the Resurrection.

THE EGG

The egg is used in much the same meaning as the butterfly. The chick emerging from the shell symbolizes the Resurrection from the Tomb.

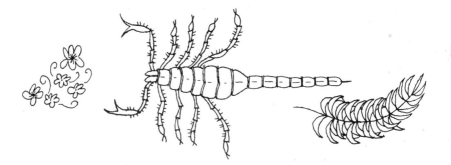

THE SCORPION

The scorpion is considered a symbol of evil rather than of good. It has a poisonous bite and therefore is used in connection with Judas, the betrayer of Christ. It is also symbolic of the soldiers who scourged Jesus before they crucified Him.

THE THISTLE AND ILEX

The thistle and ilex have been used as symbolic of the Crucifixion. For it has been said of both of them that they were used to make the Crown of Thorns.

[84]

THE HAWTHORN TREE

In Czechoslovakia, the hawthorn tree is said to weep on Holy Thursday. This saying comes from the legend that the Crown of Thorns worn by Jesus on the Cross was made from the thorns of the hawthorn tree.

THE REED

Another symbol which is used for the Crucifixion is the reed. The Gospel tells us that a sponge soaked in vinegar was placed on the end of a reed and offered to Jesus while he was on the Cross.

It was also believed that the reed was used to fashion a scourge with which to smite the Lord.

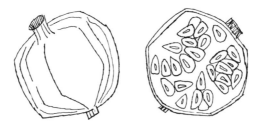

THE POMEGRANATE

The use of the pomegranate to signify the Resurrection really has its origin in the old legend of Proserpina and the return of Spring. Proserpina, daughter of Ceres, goddess of the earth, had been kidnapped by King Pluto. Although she was finally returned to her mother, because she had eaten six pomegranate seeds she had to remain with Pluto for six months each year in his underground kingdom. This ancient Roman legend was transferred to Christian legend to signify that the Lord had power to burst forth from the Tomb (Pluto's kingdom) and live again.

THE ANEMONE

The anemone is one of the flowers often seen in great paintings of the Crucifixion. The story is that these little flowers, on the night of the Crucifixion, sprang up all around the base of the Cross. On each of the petals was a red spot which symbolized the blood of Christ. From that day on, anemones have always been marked in this fashion.

THE PALM TREE

Whenever the Romans were victorious in battle, the way of the returning heroes was strewn with palms. This was the accepted custom of reception, so when Jesus rode into Jerusalem on what we now call Palm Sunday, palms were used to give him a joyous welcome.

THE ASPEN TREE

Two different legends tell of the tree whose wood was used to make the Cross on which Christ was crucified. One such story is of the aspen tree. Some say that when a tree was to be chosen for the Cross, none of the others would allow themselves to be used. As soon as the axe touched one it would crumble and fall into thousands of splinters. But the aspen permitted itself to be used. Afterwards, when it realized what it had done, its leaves began to tremble. And from that time on, aspen leaves have never ceased to quiver.

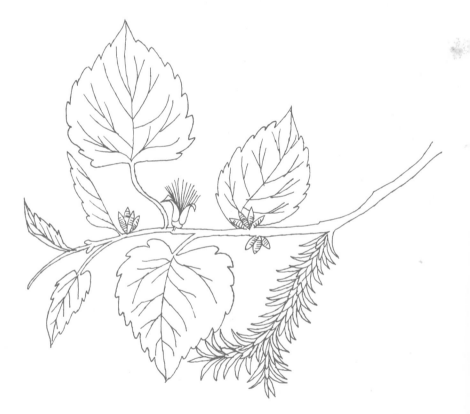

THE DOGWOOD TREE

The second legend is of the dogwood tree. Many years ago, when Jesus lived on the earth, the dogwood tree was tall and sturdy like the oak. Because of its great strength, it was selected as the one from which the Cross that was to bear Jesus would be made. The dogwood was very distressed when it heard this and grieved deeply. Jesus was sensitive to the sorrows of all persons and things, and He understood the dogwood's grief. So He told it that because of its pity for Him, nevermore would it be put to such use again. Henceforth it would no longer be rugged and stand straight. It would be instead crooked and slender. It would bear delicate blossoms which would be in the shape of a cross. On each petal at the sides would be dark red stains resembling nailprints. The center of the flower would be marked as though with a crown of thorns. And the dogwood tree would hereafter be a reminder to all people of Christ who died for them on the Cross.

[89]

THE FAIRY STONES OF VIRGINIA

There is one Easter legend which had its origin in the Blue Ridge region of Virginia. Stones may be found there which are in the shape of crosses. Their natural color varies from dark reddish brown to brownish black. The legend tells how the fairies of Virginia wept bitterly when they heard about the Crucifixion of Christ. When their tears fell on the earth they crystallized into these pebbles which are known as the Fairy Stones of Virginia. Superstitious people believe that if you wear one you will be protected against witchcraft, sickness, and all disasters.

THE QUEST OF THE HOLY GRAIL

A legend

In the Gospels it is related that after Jesus was crucified there came to Pilate a rich man of Arimathaea called Joseph. He asked Pilate for the body of Jesus and laid it in his own tomb which he had hewn out of rock. Now this Joseph was one of Christ's disciples, and for many years after the Lord had ascended into heaven he went about preaching the gospel. But the followers of Jesus were persecuted; according to a legend, Joseph was forced to flee his native country, and he departed for Britain. Because of his goodness, the legend relates, Britain became a holy land and was singled out for many miracles.

Among the legends concerning these miracles which have come down to us is that of the appearance of the Holy Grail from time to time. The Holy Grail was the cup from which Jesus drank at the time of the Last Supper, and it was said that Joseph of Arimathaea had brought it with him to Britain. After his death Britain sank into pagan ways, and for many years no one saw the Grail. But when King Arthur had won the country back to Christianity, the Holy Grail began once again to appear before people occasionally.

Sometimes it might appear on the altar during the celebration of the Eucharist. Sometimes it might appear before a devout man kneeling in prayer. Whenever it appeared it was covered with samite, a silk cloth interwoven with threads of gold or silver, and it was accompanied by a band of angels who bore it in their hands.

No one knew, however, where the Grail was kept and no one had ever seen it uncovered. But everyone felt that he would indeed be blessed who would be allowed to behold it. The story of the quest of the Holy Grail is one of the many legends told about King Arthur and his Knights of the Round Table.

Among the knights of King Arthur was a young man, Sir Galahad. When Galahad had come to the court it was said that he was a descendant of Joseph of Arimathaea. Many years before, Merlin the wizard had placed in the river a stone which had a sword sticking out of it. In the pommel of the sword, written in precious stones and gold, were these words: *Never shall man take me hence, but only by he whose side I ought to hang, and he shall be the best knight in the world.* Although several knights had tried to take the sword they had failed. When Galahad arrived at the court, King Arthur had led him to the river and Galahad had easily removed the sword from the stone. When the other knights beheld this feat they knew that Galahad was indeed a very special person.

One evening, as all the knights were feasting in the great hall, there was a great crashing of thunder. After it had ceased, a blinding light filled the room. In the midst of this there appeared

the Holy Grail covered with white samite. But the light was so bright that no one could actually see the Grail nor who bore it, although they knew they were in its presence.

The knights were silent for a moment after the Grail had disappeared from view. Then King Arthur arose and spoke.

"Let us give thanks to God that he has seen fit to bless us by the appearance of the Holy Grail at our feast."

When he had finished speaking and sat down Sir Gawaine came forward and, standing in front of King Arthur, begged permission to speak.

"It is true," he said, "that we have been blessed by the appearance of the Grail. But it being so closely covered, we cannot truly say that we have seen it. Therefore, I vow that on this very next morning I shall depart in quest of the Grail, nor shall I return until I have beheld it uncovered."

After Sir Gawaine had returned to his place at the Round Table, many of the other knights arose and took the same vow. On hearing them, King Arthur grieved, for he knew that never again would he have the fellowship of all his knights together.

Among the knights who left Camelot the next morning were Sir Launcelot, one of King Arthur's most honored knights, and Sir Galahad.

Although Sir Galahad carried the sword he had plucked from the stone, he had no shield. It happened that on the fourth day after he had set out from Camelot he met Sir Bagdemagus and Sir Uwaine, and they journeyed together until they came to an abbey. They lodged there with the monks that night, and the next morning one of the monks led them behind the altar and showed them a shield hanging there. It was white and in its center was a cross of red. The monk told them it was to be worn only by the most worthy knight in the world.

When Sir Bagdemagus saw the shield he was filled with an overwhelming desire to wear it.

"I know you do not consider me worthy," he told the monk,

"but I beseech you to let me wear it." Then turning to Sir Galahad, he said, "Stay you here until you see how I fare." Sir Galahad promised to do that, and Sir Bagdemagus departed wearing the shield.

Not long after he was on his way he met another knight who engaged him in conflict, and Sir Bagdemagus was defeated. His conqueror took the shield from him and returned it to the abbey. Thereupon the monk said to Sir Galahad, who had remained there as he had promised, "Sometimes it is necessary to allow persons to prove to themselves their own unworthiness. But you, who are known to be a descendant of Joseph of Arimathaea, whose shield this once was, and who bear Merlin's sword, should be its possessor. Take it and wear it with honor."

So Sir Galahad took the shield and, after thanking the monk, departed from the monastery and continued on his journey.

Now there had been one hundred and fifty knights who had departed from Camelot in search of the Grail. Of this number many were killed, and only a few returned to the Court of King Arthur. One of those who came close to beholding the Grail was Sir Launcelot.

Some time after Sir Launcelot had departed on his journey, he had a vision which told him to board a certain ship. He found the ship where he had been told it would be and got on it as he had been instructed. Although it had neither oars nor sail it bore him swiftly to a castle. He left the ship and was approaching close to the castle when he saw two lions guarding the entrance. He was frightened and drew his sword for protection. Just then a dwarf came through the doorway.

"Have you so little faith in your own worthiness," he said sharply, "that you fear you may be destroyed before finding what you seek?"

Having spoken, the dwarf disappeared again within the castle. Whereupon Sir Launcelot, ashamed that he had behaved in so cowardly a fashion, entered through the doorway without meeting any harm from the lions.

Once inside he wandered freely from room to room but at last came to a door which was locked. Inside a voice was heard singing more sweetly than he had ever heard anyone sing before. Somehow Sir Launcelot knew that the Holy Grail was in that room.

Then Sir Launcelot fell on his knees and prayed, "Dear Lord, I beseech you to let me, unworthy as I am, see, now, that for which I have so long sought."

After he had finished he remained kneeling, and then the door opened and Sir Launcelot beheld a room so filled with light that at first he was blinded. As though from a great distance he heard a voice saying, "Arise, Sir Launcelot, and depart quickly, for you know you are unworthy of beholding that which you seek."

But Sir Launcelot heeded not and, getting to his feet, entered the room. In its center he beheld a table of silver on which was the Holy Grail covered with red samite, and surrounding it were many angels. Sir Launcelot approached, but before he could get near he felt a breath of air so hot that he was overcome and fell to the floor. Then hands picked him up and he was carried from the room and laid outside the door, where he was found later.

For twenty-four days and nights he lay unconscious, but he finally recovered. Sir Launcelot realized then that he had come as close to the Holy Grail as he ever could, so sadly he returned to Camelot.

In the meantime Sir Galahad had met Sir Bois and Sir Percivale, and they decided to continue on their quest together. Eventually they arrived at the same castle where Sir Launcelot had seen the covered Grail. They, too, found the room with the silver table and saw the angels surrounding the Grail.

But when they had entered the room they heard a voice saying, "Approach the table, Sir Galahad, lift up this Holy Vessel, and bear it from this place. Although you are beholding what you so

desired, you have not seen it as clearly as you will in the City of Sarras in a more spiritual place. Take with you your two companions and my blessings go with all of you."

So Sir Galahad and the other two knights did as they were directed. They took ship and after many days arrived at Sarras. But when the Lord of the City of Sarras heard of their coming he was afraid they had come to seize his power, and he ordered them to be thrown into prison. All the time they were in prison they were sustained in strength by the presence of the Holy Grail.

At the end of a year the ruler of the city fell ill, and before his death he ordered the knights to be set free. When the council of the city met to elect a new king a voice spoke to them.

"Select for your king the knight among the three whom you have just freed who is the youngest."

The men of the council who were followers of Jesus Christ knew that He had made His wishes known to them. So they selected Sir Galahad to be their king.

Sir Galahad ruled the city for a year, and on the anniversary of his becoming king he went into the chapel to pray. In the chapel he found that the Holy Grail, which had been placed on the altar, was uncovered and was surrounded by a group of angels. In front was a Bishop beginning to celebrate the Eucharist. When he was finished he called to Sir Galahad.

"Come forward, my son," he said, "and behold that which you have so long desired."

Sir Galahad approached the altar, and when he saw at last the Holy Grail he knelt reverently before it. Suddenly, as he was kneeling, his soul departed from his body and was borne to heaven by the angels. And a hand reached down and took the Holy Grail and carried it, too, to heaven.

So the quest was ended, and never from that time on would any other man be blessed by beholding the Holy Grail.

EASTER MUSIC

The Music of Easter

Sing unto God, sing praises to his name (Psalm 68).
*All the earth shall worship thee . . . they shall sing to
thy name* (Psalm 66).

All through the book of Psalms we read verses like those quoted above. From the very earliest times, whenever people gathered together to worship, singing played an important part. Music has always been one way of creating a feeling of unity. For example, there is nothing that so stirs an assembly of persons to patriotism as singing its national anthem. Music has the power to make one feel either sad or joyful.

When congregations first began to worship together in Christ's name it was quite natural, therefore, that music would be a part of the service. Those early Christians, with their Jewish backgrounds, were accustomed to singing hymns glorifying God. But after the advent of Jesus they couldn't be happy with just the Hebrew Psalms. They had to express their faith in Christ, and so it was necessary to write new hymns of praise.

As time went on, different kinds of music developed. There were chants which were sung by the priests and the choirs as part of the service itself. There were hymns in which the whole congregation joined. And there were the great oratorios and Passion music performed by trained singers and accompanied by organ and orchestra.

It is not known who wrote many of the early hymns. Probably they were changed from time to time and are quite different now from when they were first written. Some were composed to celebrate special events in the Christian year such as Christmas, Palm Sunday, Good Friday, and Easter. Others were of a more general nature, to be sung on any occasion. In later years when many Protestant churches were established there were some hymns that were composed especially for congregations of one particular denomination. But the best loved and most familiar are used by all churches of the Christian faith.

Oratorios and Passion music were a later development of church music. St. Philip Neri, a priest who lived in Italy around the middle of the sixteenth century, is given credit for composing the first oratorio. It came about in this manner.

Father Neri was holding a series of daily meetings in a small chapel of the church called the oratory. In order to make these meetings more interesting and to attract more persons to them, Father Neri arranged for certain scenes of the Bible to be enacted, accompanied by hymn singing. And from that time on, whenever music was used with a dramatized Bible story it was called an oratorio, taking its name from the place where it was first performed.

Passion music was developed first in Germany. Although it, too, was a combination of Bible stories and music, it differed from the oratorio in that it kept within one theme—the Crucifixion and the Resurrection of our Lord. Oratorios are sometimes given in places other than churches but Passion music is so sacred in nature that it is never performed except in a church.

Opera, a still more dramatic form of story with musical accompaniment, is not usually considered in a discussion of church music. It is always performed in a theater rather than a church. But because Richard Wagner's opera *Parsifal* is often performed during Holy Week, it is included here in our section on Music of Easter.

GEORGE FRIDERIC HANDEL AND "MESSIAH"

On Wednesday, March 23, 1743, at the Theatre Royal in Covent Garden, London, King George II was among those in attendance at the first English performance of George Frideric Handel's oratorio *Messiah*. Handel, himself, was conducting, and as the music reached its great climax in the singing of the "Hallelujah Chorus" the king was so moved by its magnificence that he got to his feet. Since no Englishman remains seated when his monarch is standing, everyone in the audience arose too. And thus was the tradition established of standing during the rendition of the "Hallelujah Chorus" of *Messiah*.

George Frideric Handel was born in Halle, Saxony, on February 23, 1685. His father was ambitious for his son and had plans for him to study law. But young George Frideric had other ideas. From the time he was very young he could think of nothing but music.

As with all great men, stories are told about them which may or may not be founded on fact. One such story is told about Handel. It is said that his father was so incensed over his young son's determination to play that he forbade him to have any instruction in music. But some friends, sympathetic with the boy's ambition, had a spinet smuggled into the attic of his home. And late at night, with the strings deadened with cloth, the little boy practiced to his heart's content.

When George was seven years old his father took him with him to Weissenfels to visit his brother Karl who was the valet to Duke Johann Adolf. In some way the Duke learned of the boy's ability to perform on the organ and insisted on hearing him. He was so impressed with the lad's ability to improvise that he urged his father to let him study music. George's father was most unhappy. Music was the last profession in the world he wanted for his son. Although George Handel was not a subject of the Duke, he realized th. t to ignore what amounted to a royal command might cause considerable trouble. So he had no choice but to comply.

At last George Frideric's dream came true and he was allowed to study music. He was fortunate in having a teacher who could give him lessons not only in organ but in singing, clavier, oboe, violin, and composition. In three years, however, his progress was so rapid that his teacher, who was wise as well as talented, informed George's father that he had taught him all he could. So young George, in 1696, was taken to Berlin, where he immediately became a sensation in the musical circles of that city.

When George Frideric was twelve years old his father died. And because his affection and respect for his father was so strong, the young lad determined to carry out his father's wishes and study law. He entered Halle University, and during the next few years financed his law education by being organist in a church.

By the time he was eighteen, having given law a trial, he was convinced that it definitely was not for him. So he withdrew from the University, resigned his church position, and departed for Hamburg. At Hamburg he had no trouble in securing a position as second violinist in the Opera House.

One of his friends at this time was Johann Mattheson, the opera's leading tenor, who also directed the opera when he was not on stage singing. Because of Handel's ability, he was permitted to direct the orchestra when Mattheson was on stage. But one night Handel refused to turn over his baton when Mattheson was ready to relieve him. Mattheson was furious and flew into a tremendous rage. Handel immediately flew into one which equaled Mattheson's. Indeed, it grew so serious they decided there was only one way to resolve it—a duel. Fortunately the duel didn't have fatal consequences. Mattheson's sword touched a button on Handel's coat and the contest was declared over. Probably both of the contestants were secretly relieved that it ended the way it did. But although in later years, when Mattheson sang in one of Handel's operas, the friendship was revived, it never was quite the same as it was previous to their quarrel.

The year 1707 found Handel touring Italy, going first to Florence, then to Rome, and finally to Venice. After three years of travel he decided to settle in Hanover. The Elector of Hanover was Georg Ludwig. He was very fond of music and became interested in the young talented musician who was establishing such a reputation for himself. But Handel was not ready to settle down yet and was anxious to visit England. So Georg Ludwig gave him permission to do so, and he stayed in that country for a year. In 1712 he again asked for and received permission to revisit

England. This time somehow the visit lengthened out, and he was to make London his home until his death forty-six years later.

In 1714, Queen Anne of England died and Handel's former patron, Georg Ludwig, Elector of Hanover, was proclaimed King George I. King George had never forgiven Handel for deserting Hanover and would have nothing to do with the young man who had become so popular in London. Some of Handel's friends were so disturbed because of this that they tried to arrange things so he would once again be in favor.

There are two versions which tell how this was accomplished. One story is that Francesco Geminiani, a greatly admired violinist, was invited to play at court. He consented with the provision that he could bring his own accompanist. His choice was Handel. Thus it was that Handel got his chance to be received at court and was once again restored to his monarch's favor.

The other and more colorful version is that the royal household was planning an elaborate party which was to take place on a barge sailing down the Thames River. Handel had a good friend at court who arranged that there should be an accompanying barge carrying musicians. He invited Handel to compose the music to be played and to direct the orchestra. When the king heard the music he was so impressed that he asked who had composed it. On being told it was Handel he sent for him, congratulated him, and restored him to favor once again. The music which was played that day later came to be known as *Water Music*.

As Handel grew older he must have presented an imposing appearance. It was the fashion of that day for men to wear tight-fitting knee breeches and long flowing coats. One portrait shows Handel sitting very erect and wearing what appears to be a very elaborate velvet suit. His tightly curled wig hangs below his shoulders. It is said that he walked with a peculiar gait, probably caused by his bow legs and his excessive fat. Indeed, he is described as having not only two chins but three! Although good humored, he had a quick temper. The story is told that one day, at a rehearsal of one of his operas, the prima donna refused to sing a certain aria as he wanted it done. Whereupon he seized her around the waist and told her she would sing it as he wished or he would drop her from the window. Meekly, she complied with his request. Handel was very emotional and sometimes wept as he composed. Generosity was one of his great virtues, and many of his concerts were given for the benefit of the Foundling Hospital. He was so interested in this particular charity that in his will he bequeathed to it a copy of the score and all parts of his oratorio *Messiah.*

Handel's life was a succession of ups and downs. Sometimes he was popular, and sometimes his popularity seemed to be in a decline. In 1741, attendance at his operas became so small that they were discontinued. On April 8 of that year he gave his last operatic concert.

It was in August that same year that he began working on *Messiah.* The Bible verses that were used as a text for this oratorio were chosen for him by Charles Jennens, Jr. Handel's friendship with Jennens had begun about 1735. Jennens was a very eccentric person, and colorful stories have been told about him. He loved luxury and indulged himself in it to the point of being ridiculous. If he was going only a short distance from home, he would arrive in a coach drawn by four horses. Before he would alight from his carriage, a servant would carefully sweep the places where Jennens would walk.

Handel was particularly inspired by the selection of verses Jennens gave him and, working feverishly, he finished composing the music within twenty-three days. Legend has said that one time when a servant brought him food he found the composer working on what was to be the "Hallelujah Chorus" with tears streaming down his cheeks.

Messiah was performed first in Dublin, April 13, 1742. The notices which were sent out previous to the opening requested ladies not to wear hoops and gentlemen to leave their swords at home. Evidently space was at a premium, and hoops and swords took up too much room!

Although the first London performance was a great success, *Messiah* did not prove to be popular. After three performances it was not produced again until 1745, and then four years elapsed before it was to be heard again. Probably the reason was that there was a strong feeling among many people that a work so deeply religious should not be performed in a theater.

On April 6, 1759, Handel directed *Messiah* for the last time in Covent Garden. For some years he had been in poor health, and his eyes were so bad that he was nearly blind. That evening after the performance he was taken ill, and during the night of Good Friday, April 13, 1759, George Frideric Handel died. He was buried in Westminster Abbey, and a statue of him marks the place of burial.

Although *Messiah* was never extremely popular during Handel's lifetime, it is without doubt the composition by which he is best remembered. It was first performed in the United States in New York City on January 16, 1770. In this performance *Messiah* was not given in its entirety, but in Boston on December 25, 1818, the whole oratorio was heard.

From this time it became traditional to give *Messiah* at Christmas. But in 1882, in Lindsborg, Kansas, it was performed at Eastertime. Everyone in the community took part—professional persons, laborers, housewives—all joined in. And once again the custom of giving it during the Easter season was established.

During the years which have followed its composing, *Messiah* seems more and more to express the true meaning of Easter. For it not only is the telling of the Old Testament prophecies of the coming of Christ, the Herald's announcing His birth and then Christ's life on earth, but the real meaning of the Crucifixion and Resurrection is finally summed up in an expression of man's faith in all that for which Christ stands.

JOHANN SEBASTIAN BACH AND THE "ST. MATTHEW PASSION"

After reading about the lives of many composers of great music, certain pictures come into one's mind when their names are mentioned. The name Mozart reminds one person of a portrait of a young boy fingering the strings of a violin. Someone else may see him performing in a concert hall on the harpsichord before an audience greatly impressed with this child prodigy. One thinks of Beethoven as an older man, stone deaf, composing beautiful symphonies for great orchestras. Wagner's stirring music can make one imagine a huge opera stage with the Valkyries galloping furiously along. But when the name Bach is mentioned, somehow the deep tones of a church organ can be distinctly heard.

At the time of the two great festivals of the Christian year, Christmas and Easter, people go to church not only to hear again the story of Christ but also to hear the music which was composed especially for these occasions.

Easter is a joyous time because on that day we celebrate the Resurrection of Christ. Good Friday, which precedes it, is a solemn occasion because that is the day on which He was crucified. So it is quite natural that while the music used in churches on Easter morning is joyous, that which is used the week before is solemn. Palm Sunday is often reserved for the performance of the *St. Matthew Passion,* composed by Johann Sebastian Bach.

The story of the *St. Matthew Passion* follows the Bible text. The first part tells of the chief priests' decision to arrest Jesus. The Lord's Supper, Christ's prayers on the Mount of Olives, and finally the betrayal by Judas follow. In the second half we are told of the trial of Jesus, the judgment of Pontius Pilate, and at the end the Crucifixion of our Lord.

It is interesting to know that many musical compositions which we now consider great were not always received with favor when they were first heard. The *St. Matthew Passion* is one of these. The reason generally accepted for this is that the music is dramatic, and people of that period thought it was not suitable to be performed in a church. And yet, because of its sacred and deeply religious theme, it could not be performed anywhere else.

The first performance of this great piece of music was given in Leipzig, Germany, on Good Friday in 1729. At the time Bach had a position as director of music at the St. Thomas School in that city. The people who first heard it did not receive it favorably, and for about a hundred years no one seemed aware of it. An interesting story is told how the *St. Matthew Passion* came to be rediscovered.

One of Bach's descendants, in disposing of his belongings, had taken a pile of old manuscripts to a cheesemonger's shop. Quite by accident a collector of items such as these happened in and in going through the manuscripts discovered the score of the *St. Matthew Passion*. He acquired it and later showed it to one of his pupils, Felix Mendelssohn. Mendelssohn, who later became a famous composer, liked it so much that he wanted to copy it. At first his teacher wouldn't allow him to do so. Later on he relented and gave Mendelssohn a copy of the score. It was Felix Mendelssohn who arranged for it to be given again. In 1829, at a concert in Berlin in honor of Bach, the public once again heard the stirring music of the *St. Matthew Passion*. This was just one hundred years after its first performance.

Johann Sebastian Bach was born in Eisenach in Thuringia, Germany, on March 21, 1685. He came from a family of musicians, and it is said that there were so many of them that the word *Bach* came to mean the same as *musician*.

Even when Johann was a very small boy he loved music and was very happy when his father gave him instruction. One of his greatest delights was to go to the village church and listen to the organist practice.

Johann was nine years old when his mother died. His father remarried but died shortly afterward. Johann was sent to live with Christoph, an older married brother, who lived in the town of Ohrdruf. The story is told that because of Johann's great talent and because his progress in music soon surpassed his brother's, Christoph became very jealous of Johann. Christoph was the possessor of some fine musical manuscripts, and leaving his room quietly late at night, Johann would get these manuscripts and copy them. One night as he was in the midst of this task he was surprised by his brother, who angrily took away from him all he had copied.

The year that Johann was fifteen, he desired greatly to go to Lüneburg, where he hoped to obtain employment. At first Christoph was not in favor of this plan but, after much pleading by Johann, finally gave his consent. A friend, Georg Erdmann, accompanied Johann. The two lads had no money for traveling expenses so they cheerfully set forth on their two-week journey on foot. Just as they were ready to depart, Christoph made Johann happy by giving him the manuscript he had taken from him so long ago.

When the boys reached Lüneburg Johann obtained a job singing in the choir of the Church of St. Michael. Besides singing, this gave him an opportunity to study all kinds of music—composition, organ, clavier, and violin. It was not long before people became aware of his exceptional talents, and he was offered the position of assistant choir director. Although his work kept him very busy, Bach was never one to miss an opportunity to learn by hearing others perform. It was nothing for him to walk thirty miles to Hamburg to hear some well-known organist play.

Of course the fame of this young man became more widespread, and when he was only eighteen the younger brother of the reigning Duke asked him to be the viola player in his private orchestra.

This satisfied him for a time, but Johann Sebastian Bach was not content to settle down in one place for long unless it offered him a chance to improve his ability to perform and also an opportunity to study. So the next years find him in several different positions. During this period he married his beautiful cousin, Maria Barbara.

Then he was appointed organist at the Ducal chapel in Weimar and remained there for nine years. Much of his fine organ music was composed at this time. He was also much in demand for performances in neighboring cities, and finally he came to the attention of Prince Leopold of Cöthen. When Leopold invited him to become director of music at his court, Bach accepted. This was the period when he wrote many of his works for orchestra and solo instruments.

Leopold often invited Bach to accompany him on journeys, and on returning from one such trip Bach learned that his wife Maria Barbara had died, leaving him with four small children to care for. Their marriage had been a happy one and, although Bach grieved deeply for his wife, the next year he married Anna Magdelena, the daughter of a musician friend. From these two marriages Bach became the father of twenty children.

Shortly after Bach's second marriage, Prince Leopold married. His wife was totally disinterested in music, and she persuaded Leopold to pay less and less attention to Bach. Requests for concerts became fewer, and Bach grew restless and unhappy. When a position as director of music became vacant in the St. Thomas School in Leipzig, Bach applied for it and held it during the rest of his life. Johann Sebastian Bach died July 28, 1750, at the age of sixty-five.

Bach is described as a man who, though he had a happy disposition and a sense of humor, was completely dedicated to his work. He was esteemed as a great performer and his reputation as an organist was well known, but during his lifetime he was never recognized as a great composer. His music was not even well enough thought of to be carefully preserved. It is said that his widow, needing money badly, sold a bundle of his manuscripts for forty dollars.

But the years have changed all that. Today there are choirs devoted entirely to the performance of the music of Johann Sebastian Bach. And each year in Bethlehem, Pennsylvania, he is honored at the famous Bach Festival. The great humanitarian, Albert Schweitzer, is noted for being an authority on Bach and his music. Great orchestras perform his music. And on Palm Sunday many persons are indeed fortunate if they hear the *St. Matthew Passion*. Somehow it seems sad that Johann Sebastian Bach, who loved music so deeply and who has given so much pleasure to the world, never knew how much he would be appreciated. For in musical history he is considered one of the most important composers of all times.

RICHARD WAGNER AND "PARSIFAL"

It is the week before Easter. The lights in the opera house have been dimmed. A hush falls over the audience as the orchestra finishes the last strains of the overture to the first act. Whether they are dressed in formal evening wear, costly furs, and jewels and occupying boxes in the first and second tiers, or whether they are dressed informally and sitting in the family circle or standing in the back, there is one thing the people of this audience have in common. They enjoy good music and they are here for one of the special treats of the opera season. The curtain rises slowly on a scene laid in a woodland glade. *Parsifal,* considered by some to be Richard Wagner's finest opera, is about to begin.

To enjoy *Parsifal* to its fullest extent it is helpful to know the background of the operatic story. Although it concerns the search for the Holy Grail, Wagner based his story on a different legend from that told by Malory in the King Arthur stories. The setting of *Parsifal* is northern Spain rather than England.

The Holy Grail was the cup from which Christ drank at the Last Supper. It was kept in the Castle of Monsalvat and entrusted to a knight whose name was Titurel. Besides the Grail, the spear which was used to pierce the side of Christ when He was crucified was also kept in the castle. Many knights had vowed to help Titurel guard the Grail and devoted their lives to this mission. Many others wished to join them, but only those who had led pure lives were accepted.

One of those who had been turned away was Klingsor, a magician, and because of this he sought revenge. Near the castle was a desert area, and he turned it into a beautiful garden. He peopled it with sirens whose purpose it was to lure the knights guarding the Grail into sinful living.

One of the sirens was a maiden called Kundry whom Klingsor

had enchanted. Klingsor achieved his greatest triumph when Amfortas, the son of Titurel, came under her spell. Amfortas was carrying the sacred spear at the time, and it was taken from him by Klingsor. Klingsor pierced Amfortas' side with it, and there was no known remedy that would heal the wound. Because it never healed, it was a constant reminder to Amfortas that he had sinned and would be unworthy of beholding the Grail. However, it had been said that someday a healing would be brought about by a "guileless fool" who had been made wise by understanding the suffering of his fellow men.

When the curtain goes up on Act I of *Parsifal,* the knights of Amfortas are seen in the forest near the castle. Amfortas has just been carried past them on a litter, and they are discussing his plight. Suddenly their conversation is interrupted as a wild swan falls dead at their feet. A moment later a youth approaches to claim his prize. The knights chide the young man for killing on sacred ground. When the youth hears that he has been guilty of this he is filled with remorse, breaks his bow and arrows, and throws them away.

The knights question him, and he tells them his name is Parsifal but that he knows nothing of his origin nor who his mother was. Suddenly Kundry appears. She is clothed in a coarse garment and her hair is disheveled, making her look half wild. She tells the knights that she knows about Parsifal and that when his mother had reared him she cast him forth, saying he was a fool.

Parsifal becomes very angry when he hears her say this and rushes toward her. But the knights restrain him from doing her harm. They think perhaps he may be the "guileless fool" sent to heal the wound of Amfortas, and they ask him to accompany them to the temple where Amfortas guards the Grail. Parsifal agrees to go. When he sees Amfortas, although moved to pity at his plight, he does not understand his agony. Angered at this, Gurnemanz, one of the knights, drives Parsifal from the temple.

Act II takes place in the palace of Klingsor. Klingsor has heard that Parsifal is approaching the palace and he, too, thinks Parsifal is the one destined to heal Amfortas' wound. He resolves to ensnare him by having him fall under the charms of Kundry as Amfortas did.

Parsifal arrives at the palace ramparts and, on climbing over them, finds himself in a beautiful garden filled with flowers. Kundry appears before him and under the enchantment of Klingsor is most beautiful. Parsifal is overcome with her beauty and sinks to his knees. As they embrace he feels a sudden stab in his side, and it reminds him of Amfortas. He feels a strong pity for him and speaks his name. As he does so, an overpowering hatred of Kundry seizes him and he pushes her aside. Klingsor appears with the sacred spear and hurls it in anger at Parsifal. But the spear doesn't touch him. It hangs suspended above his head, and Parsifal seizes it and makes the sign of the Cross. There is a sound as though of an earthquake. The castle crumbles to the ground, and the garden becomes a desert. Kundry lies among the ruins.

When Act III opens, many years have passed. Parsifal has been

seeking the resting place of the Holy Grail. He is still carrying the sacred spear, although many have tried to take it from him. He enters the forest which is near the temple where the Holy Grail is being guarded by Amfortas and his knights. Parsifal meets an old knight outside the temple and recognizes him as Gurnemanz, who had driven him forth so long ago. With Gurnemanz is Kundry. When Klingsor and his castle were destroyed, she was released from her enchantment. Since that time, as atonement, she has devoted her life to serving others. Parsifal is impressed by her penitence and baptizes her. He then bades her come with him into the temple. Parsifal is dressed like the guardians of the Grail, so they are able to pass into the temple unquestioned. They finally come to the inner room where the Grail is kept and find Amfortas, who has been carried there on his litter.

Titurel has just died and is borne by his knights in solemn procession into the room. The knights realize that Titurel died without having beheld the Grail and they beg Amfortas to uncover it. But Amfortas knows he is unworthy and in his grief implores his knights to kill him so he can atone for his sin and they will then be able to unveil the Grail themselves.

Parsifal then steps forward and touches Amfortas' wound with the spear, and immediately it is healed. The knights realize that Parsifal is the one who should rightfully be the keeper of the Grail. Parsifal approaches the Grail and uncovers it for the first time. As he does so a white dove floats down and hovers over his head. A white light floods the temple, and the Grail turns from a pale pink to blood red. Kundry, overcome at the sight, falls lifeless to the ground. The voices of knights and angels join together in a song of praise for the Redeemer, and the final curtain descends.

Richard Wagner had considered *Parsifal* to be so sacred in character that in his will he forbade a stage performance to be given except in the opera house at Bayreuth which was devoted entirely to Wagnerian operas. But in 1903, Heinrich Conried, director of the Metropolitan Opera in New York City, decided to disregard this wish of Wagner's. An elaborate production of *Parsifal* was staged. This so enraged Wagner's widow and his family that they forbade anyone who took part in the performance ever to appear on the stage at Bayreuth.

Today we are so familiar with music from Wagnerian operas that we accept it without question. But it was not always so. Wagner's music was not understood at first, and many opera companies would not present any of his operas. Of course there were some who did like them, and for many years the controversy raged over whether the music was good or bad. The mention of the name *Wagner* could be counted upon to start an argument in almost any group of musicians.

Wagner had an idea for opera that was new in his day. He felt that dramatic form was as important as music. And he added something else, too. Each of his characters or a certain mood could be identified by the same musical phrase or motif. This had never been done before and seemed revolutionary at the time. Most Wagnerian operas are difficult to sing because they are long, and it takes a singer with physical endurance to perform them.

Besides writing operas which were criticized, Richard Wagner, himself, was a person who seemed to invite people either to like or dislike him very much. He was born in Leipzig, Germany, May 22, 1813, the ninth child of Friedrich William and Johanna Wagner. His father, a clerk in the Municipal Court in Leipzig, died during a typhoid epidemic when Richard was very young. Not long afterward his mother married Ludwig Geyer, a close friend of the family.

Ludwig Geyer was very fond of his young stepson, Richard. Geyer was an actor and often took Richard to rehearsals with him. So it was at an early age that Richard got his first taste and liking for the theater.

Richard was never a very good student at school. He was not

lazy, but he always seemed to resent having to work at anything that was not to his liking. He was full of fun and fond of playing pranks. Even when young he loved to write plays. All of them were tragedies, and by the end he had always killed off all his characters.

Early in life he showed an interest in music, but studying theory was irksome to him. It was for this reason that his early operas and symphonies were not successful. He persuaded one conductor to perform one of his overtures, and it sounded so terrible that the audience laughed all the way through it.

By the time Wagner was twenty-one he had a position as conductor of a small operatic theater in Magdeburg. He had written an opera and resolved to produce it himself. At the first performance the audience was fairly large. But at the second there were only Wagner, his landlady, and her husband. To top it all off, just before the performance was to begin the prima donna and her husband had a quarrel which ended so disastrously that she was unable to go on the stage! So the manager told the audience of three there would be no performance. Thus ended Wagner's first excursion into the operatic field.

Wagner's personal life also was a subject to cause much discussion. Although at the age of twenty-two he married Minna Planer, a young actress, their married life was never completely happy. After twenty-five years, Minna left him and a few years later she died. Wagner's second wife was Cosima, daughter of Franz Liszt.

Richard Wagner died in Venice, Italy, February 13, 1883, at the age of seventy. At the time of his death he had composed thirteen operas, besides many pieces for orchestra, piano, and choral groups.

Wagner is described as a man of medium stature and build. His face was deeply lined and his gray-blue eyes were brilliant and piercing. Although he was considered vain, nervous, and irritable, he had a great deal of personal magnetism that drew people to him. It is said, however, that he made more enemies than friends in his lifetime. He loved luxury, but many of his years were spent in direst poverty. When he had money, he spent it. His home was furnished with tapestries, expensive rugs, and silken draperies. He liked elaborate clothes and was said to possess at one time twenty-four dressing gowns of different colors with slippers to match.

Even though we may not approve of the personal qualities of Wagner, we must respect his genius. For he left to the world many musical masterpieces.

Parsifal was the last opera Richard Wagner composed. In it he expressed reverently, through the medium of beautiful poetry and music, the hope of the Redemption of Mankind.

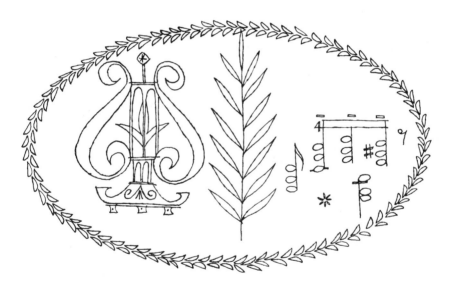

THE PALMS

O'er all the way, green palms and blossoms gay
Are strewn, this day, in festal preparation.

This beloved hymn, widely used on Palm Sunday, was written by Jean-Baptiste Faure. In his lifetime Faure was not well known as a composer, for he published but two books of songs. Rather he was known as a performer and was one of the outstanding singers of his day.

Jean-Baptiste Faure was born in Moulins, France, January 15, 1830. It was quite natural that his musical talent would be recognized, for his father was a singer in the Moulins Cathedral. When he was still very young the family moved to Paris, and he began to study singing at the age of thirteen.

By the time he was twenty-two, he had already received recognition and had won a prize for his performance.

Faure soon became celebrated for his work in both comic opera and opera. One of his finest performances was that of Mephistopheles in *Faust*. He was in demand in London and in Vienna, as well as in Paris, and was always greatly honored when he played operatic roles in those cities. Indeed, the Emperor of Austria bestowed on him the title of Imperial Chamber Singer.

Jean-Baptiste Faure died in Paris, November 9, 1914, at the age of eighty-four.

THE PALMS

BY JEAN-BAPTISTE FAURE (1830–1914)

O'er all the way, green palms and blossoms gay
Are strewn, this day, in festal preparation,
Where Jesus comes, to wipe our tears away
E'en now the throng to welcome Him prepare:

Chorus

Join all and sing, His name declare,
Let ev'ry voice resound with acclamation,
Hosanna! Praised be the Lord!
Bless Him who cometh to bring salvation!

His word goes forth, and peoples by its might
Once more regain freedom from degradation,
Humanity doth give to each his right,
While those in darkness find restored the light!

Chorus

Join all and sing, His name declare,
Let ev'ry voice resound with acclamation,
Hosanna! Praised be the Lord!
Bless Him who cometh to bring salvation!

Sing and rejoice, oh, blest Jerusalem,
Of all thy sons sing the emancipation,
Through boundless love the Christ of Bethlehem
Brings faith and hope to thee for evermore.

Chorus

Join all and sing, His name declare,
Let ev'ry voice resound with acclamation,
Hosanna! Praised be the Lord!
Bless Him who cometh to bring salvation!

RIDE ON, RIDE ON IN MAJESTY

In 1812, a young student at Oxford won the Newdigate prize for a poem entitled "Apollo Belvidere." It was considered one of the finest poems ever to receive that coveted prize, and its author was Henry Hart Milman. Henry, a brilliant student, was born in London on February 10, 1791. His father, Sir Francis Milman, was a physician at the court of King George III.

After finishing at Oxford, young Milman was appointed professor of poetry at that university. But he decided to enter the ministry and shortly afterward resigned his position at Oxford. It was during the time he was professor of poetry that he wrote some of his best-known poems.

One of them was a long dramatic work called *Fazia*. At that time there were no adequate laws to protect authors from having others use their publications as they wished. And so without Milman's knowledge his poem was performed as a play in a London theater under the title *The Italian Wife*. The excellence of the performance brought him such fame that he felt complimented and did not protest that it had been used without his permission.

Later on, when he became more involved in church affairs, he turned his attention to the writing of history and biography rather than poetry. His *History of the Jews,* published in 1830, caused so much criticism among church people that the publishers withdrew it from sale. Some years later it was revised and republished and accepted more favorably by the public. Besides his poetry and history writings, the Reverend Henry Milman contributed to literary knowledge by translating many works from Greek, Roman, and Sanskrit writings.

In 1849 he was appointed Dean of St. Paul's in London, a position he held until his death September 24, 1868.

"Ride On, Ride On in Majesty," one of thirteen hymns he wrote, appeared first in 1827. It is one of the favorite hymns to be used on Palm Sunday.

RIDE ON, RIDE ON IN MAJESTY

BY HENRY HART MILMAN (1791–1868)

Ride on! ride on in majesty!
In lowly pomp ride on to die:
O Christ, thy triumphs now begin
O'er captive death and conquered sin.

Ride on! ride on in majesty!
The angel armies of the sky
Look down with sad and wondering eyes
To see the approaching sacrifice.

Ride on! ride on in majesty!
The last and fiercest strife is nigh:
The Father on his sapphire throne
Awaits his own anointed Son.

Ride on! ride on in majesty!
In lowly pomp ride on to die:
Bow thy meek head to mortal pain:
Then take, O God, thy power and reign.

One hymn often sung during the Easter season which expresses so well the Christian faith is "In the Cross of Christ I Glory." The author of this beautiful hymn was Sir John Bowring, who spent much of his life in the service of the British government. Sir John was considered a very strong diplomat and was actually feared by many people. On the other hand, he stood for social progress. He was a vigorous advocate of many reforms, such as changes in the prison laws and the abolishing of flogging in the navy. In his early years he was idealistic and was interested in freeing people who were oppressed. Indeed, once he was arrested and thrown into a French prison because he was caught carrying dispatches to the Portuguese government telling of an intended invasion of Portugal by the French. It was during this period of his life that he wrote many of his well-known hymns.

Sir John Bowring was born at Exeter, October 17, 1792. His family had been merchants for generations and interested in the woolen trade. It was natural, therefore, that he follow the same business after leaving school. He was well prepared for such a life, as he had been a student of languages. He could speak French, Italian, Spanish, Portuguese, German, and Dutch. He could also translate from the Swedish, Danish, Russian, Serbian, Polish, and Bohemian languages. Not content with this, later on in life he studied Magyar, Arabic, and Chinese. It is no wonder that he was considered the perfect person for appointment to the government.

He spent nine years representing the British government in Hong Kong. During a Chinese insurrection, the British colony was so unpopular that someone tried to kill all of them by putting arsenic in their bread. Sir John escaped serious illness but his wife was not that fortunate. She died not very long afterward from the effects of the poisoning.

The discomfort of his nine years in China did not end when he sailed for home. One more unpleasant experience awaited him. The ship on which he was traveling was wrecked, and the passengers were stranded for three days on a coral reef before help reached them.

Although he was in government service for some time after leaving China, his remaining years were quiet in comparison with the earlier ones. He was in demand as a lecturer and even addressed a huge assembly when he was eighty years old, not very long before his death. Sir John Bowring died at Exeter, November 23, 1872.

IN THE CROSS OF CHRIST I GLORY
BY SIR JOHN BOWRING (1792–1872)

In the Cross of Christ I glory;
Towering o'er the wrecks of time,
All the light of sacred story
Gathers round its head sublime.

When the woes of life o'ertake me,
Hopes deceive, and fears annoy,
Never shall the Cross forsake me!
Lo! it glows with peace and joy.

When the sun of bliss is beaming
Light and love upon my way:
From the Cross the radiance streaming
Adds more lustre to the day.

Bane and blessing, pain and pleasure,
By the Cross are sanctified;
Peace is there, that knows no measure,
Joys, that through all time abide.

In the Cross of Christ I glory;
Towering o'er the wrecks of time,
All the light of sacred story
Gathers round its head sublime.

MY FAITH LOOKS UP TO THEE

In 1831, a young schoolteacher in New York City wrote a hymn that would have made him famous if he had never written another. The young teacher was Ray Palmer, and the hymn he wrote was "My Faith Looks Up to Thee."

Ray Palmer was born in Little Compton, Rhode Island, November 12, 1808. His ancestors were Puritans and, indeed, he could claim to be a descendant of a William Palmer who joined the Plymouth Colony in 1621. Ray Palmer's father was a judge who saw to it that his son had a fine education. He first attended Phillips Andover Academy in Andover, Massachusetts, and on graduating from that school entered Yale in the class of 1830.

Upon graduation, he taught for a time in New York City and in New Haven, Connecticut, but gave up teaching to become a minister in the Congregational Church. He was active in church work for forty-three years and then retired to devote all his time to writing. Besides having several books of poetry published, he also was a contributor to religious periodicals.

He and his wife Ann Maria whom he had married in 1832 were the parents of ten children. The Reverend Ray Palmer died March 29, 1887.

MY FAITH LOOKS UP TO THEE

BY RAY PALMER (1808–1887)

My faith looks up to Thee,
Thou Lamb of Calvary,
Saviour divine:
Now hear me while I pray,
Take all my guilt away,
O let me from this day
Be wholly Thine!

May Thy rich grace impart
Strength to my fainting heart,
My zeal inspire;
As Thou hast died for me,
O may my love to Thee
Pure, warm, and changeless be,
A living fire!

While life's dark maze I tread,
And griefs around me spread,
Be Thou my Guide;
Bid darkness turn to day,
Wipe sorrow's tears away,
Nor let me ever stray
From Thee aside.

When ends life's transient dream,
When death's cold sullen stream
Shall o'er me roll,
Blest Saviour, then, in love,
Fear and distrust remove;
O bear me safe above,
A ransomed soul!

JESUS CHRIST IS RIS'N TODAY

There is a curious history about this song, perhaps the most popular of all Easter hymns. Actually no one knows who wrote it nor when it was written. No doubt it was one of those written centuries ago in Latin and translated sometime later. Down through the years, as it appeared in various hymnals, changes were made. One such change was the addition of the last verse.

It *is* known that the last verse was written by the Reverend Charles Wesley and was not intended for this hymn at all. But whoever added it thought that it suited as a very fitting ending and so it does. Charles Wesley's own Easter hymn beginning "Christ the Lord is Risen Today," is sometimes sung to the same melody as this one, and the two are often confused.

Not only is the writer of the words of "Jesus Christ Is Ris'n Today" unknown but the composer of the music is, too. In some hymnbooks the words "Lyra Davidica" are seen in the place where credit is usually given to author and composer. In 1708, a book of hymns entitled "Lyra Davidica" appeared and "Jesus Christ Is Ris'n Today" was included, along with the tune which is now used.

In other hymnbooks the name of Dr. John Worgan appears as composer, but he wasn't born until 1724, sixteen years after the publication of "Lyra Davidica."

But on Easter morning, when thousands of persons are gathered together for the sunrise service, without a thought as to who composed either words or music, voices are raised in song and joyfully they proclaim, "Jesus Christ Is Ris'n Today!"

JESUS CHRIST IS RIS'N TODAY
AUTHOR AND COMPOSER UNKNOWN
PROBABLY OF LATIN ORIGIN (14TH CENTURY)

Jesus Christ is ris'n today, Alleluia,
Our triumphant holy day, Alleluia,
Who did once upon the cross, Alleluia,
Suffer to redeem our loss. Alleluia.

Hymns of praise then let us sing, Alleluia,
Unto Christ, our heav'nly King, Alleluia,
Who endured the cross and grave, Alleluia,
Sinners to redeem and save. Alleluia.

But the pains which He endured, Alleluia,
Our salvation have procured; Alleluia;
Now above the sky He's King, Alleluia,
Where the angels ever sing. Alleluia.

Sing we to our God above, Alleluia,
Praise eternal as His love, Alleluia,
Praise Him, all ye heavenly host, Alleluia,
Father, Son, and Holy Ghost. Alleluia.

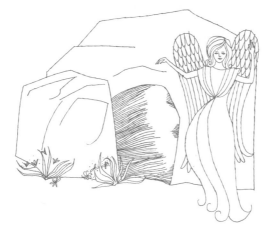

THE STRIFE IS O'ER

Some of the hymns we sing now were written so long ago, and changed so often as they were used through the years, that it is impossible to give credit to any persons for them. One such hymn which is used on Easter Sunday is "The Strife Is O'er."

It is known that its origin was Latin, but it is not known who the author was nor at what date it was written. A translation of it was made by the Reverend Francis Pott, who included it in his *Hymns Fitted to the Order of Common Prayer* published in 1859.

But although the writer of this hymn is unknown, the composer of the music to which it is sung is not. He is Palestrina, and because of the purity of his musical compositions he has been called the Prince of Music.

Palestrina was not the real name of this famous composer. It was Giovanni Pierluigi, and he was born in Palestrina, Italy, probably around 1525. As a boy he had a very fine voice, and it was decided by his family that he should be given an opportunity to study music. Although his father was not a wealthy man, his mother had inherited a plot of land, and by selling it enough money was obtained to start Giovanni on his musical career.

After studying music for some time he was appointed organist and choirmaster of his church in Palestrina. He married and prepared to settle down for life. But his musical ability had been brought to the attention of Pope Julius III, who invited him to sing in the Sistine Chapel Choir in Rome.

Although he was under contract in Palestrina, Giovanni arranged to be released and packed up his family and moved to Rome.

He held the position with the Sistine Choir for some time but was later dismissed when Pope Paul IV, who was one of the successors of Pope Julius, decided no married man could be a member of the choir.

Palestrina, as he had become known, was at first very upset. Indeed for a time he was confined to his bed. But he recovered and soon afterward was appointed chapelmaster at the Basilica of St. John Lateran.

In 1564 the Council of Trent, which had been meeting for twenty years discussing affairs of the Catholic Church, decided that the music being used in the church service was not at all suitable. There had been complaints that songs sung in the streets had been made a part of the church music. So Palestrina was asked to compose new music to be used for Mass. He complied by composing not one Mass but three. These were immediately accepted. Later on he composed many more.

In 1571, he was invited to return to the Papal Choir in the Sistine Chapel as choirmaster. And all over Italy, Palestrina became a greatly loved and honored figure. He continued to compose all his life, and his music was received with acclaim everywhere. Palestrina died on February 2, 1594.

THE STRIFE IS O'ER

AUTHOR UNKNOWN

MUSIC COMPOSED BY PALESTRINA (1525–1594)

The strife is o'er, the battle done:
The victory of Life is won:
The song of triumph has begun—
  Hallelujah!

The powers of death have done their worst,
But Christ their legions hath dispersed:
Let shout of holy joy outburst—
  Hallelujah!

The three sad days have quickly sped:
He rises glorious from the dead;
All glory to our risen Head!
  Hallelujah!

He brake the age-bound chains of hell:
The bars from heaven's high portals fell;
Let hymns of praise His triumph tell!
  Hallelujah!

Lord, by the stripes which wounded Thee,
From death's dread sting Thy servants free,
That we may live and sing to Thee,
  Hallelujah!

EASTER POEMS

PASQUE

BY ELLA YOUNG

All so frail, so white,
The blossoms on the thorn,
So pale this first daylight
On Easter morn.

Hear the cry:
"Christ is risen!"
Hear the cry:
"Christ is risen!
Our Lord sets free
The souls in prison."

The sun acclaims it
Burgeoning red:
Christ! Christ is risen
From the dead.

SONG

BY CHARLES G. BLANDEN

What trees were in Gethsemane,
  What flowers were there to scent,
When Christ for you, and Christ for me,
  Into his garden went?

The fragrant cedar tree was there,
  The lily pale and slim:
They saw his grief, they heard his prayer,
  And wept their dews for him.

And that is why the cedars green
  And why the lilies white
Do whisper of the Master's love
  In gardens, late at night.

A PRAYER IN SPRING
BY ROBERT FROST

Oh, give us pleasure in the flowers to-day;
And give us not to think so far away
As the uncertain harvest; keep us here
All simply in the springing of the year.

Oh, give us pleasure in the orchard white,
Like nothing else by day, like ghosts by night;
And make us happy in the happy bees,
The swarm dilating round the perfect trees.

And make us happy in the darting bird
That suddenly above the bees is heard,
The meteor that thrusts in with needle bill,
And off a blossom in mid-air stands still.

For this is love and nothing else is love,
The which it is reserved for God above
To sanctify to what far ends He will,
But which it only needs that we fulfill.

SONG OF EASTER

BY CELIA THAXTER

Easter lilies! Can you hear
What they whisper, low and clear?
In dewy fragrance they unfold
Their splendor sweet, their snow and gold.
Every beauty-breathing bell
News of heaven has to tell.
Listen to their mystic voice,
Hear, oh mortal, and rejoice!
Hark, their soft and heavenly chime!
Christ is risen for all time!

GREEN THINGS GROWING
BY DINAH MARIA MULOCK

Oh, the green things growing, the green things growing,
The faint, sweet smell of the green things growing!
I should like to live, whether I smile or grieve,
Just to watch the happy life of my green things growing.

Oh, the fluttering and the pattering of those green things growing!
How they talk to each other, when none of us are knowing;
In the wonderful white of the weird moonlight
Or the dim dreamy dawn when the cocks are crowing.

I love, I love them so,—my green things growing!
And I think that they love me, without false showing;
For by many a tender touch, they comfort me so much,
With the soft mute comfort of green things growing.

EASTER IN THE WOODS

BY FRANCES FROST

This dawn when the mountain-cherry lifts
its frail white bloom among dark pines,
and chipmunks flash small happy paws
along old tumbled boundary lines,
this golden morning when the vixen
nuzzles her five young foxes forth
to roll in ferns in the Easter sun,—
again the woods know soft green birth.

Snuffed by a puffball infant rabbit
are yellow violets by the spring;
among half-opened apple buds
a wood thrush tilts its head to sing.
Risen is He! And they are His,
who scamper under warm blue skies,
who nibble little fists of grass,
and gaze on earth with shy glad eyes.

SONG

BY HENRY NEVILLE MAUGHAM

There was a Knight of Bethlehem,
Whose wealth was tears and sorrows;
His men-at-arms were little lambs,
His trumpeters were sparrows;
His castle was a wooden cross,
Whereon He hung so high;
His helmet was a crown of thorns
Whose crest did touch the sky.

THE LENT LILY

BY A. E. HOUSMAN

'Tis spring; come out to ramble
   The hilly brakes around,
For under thorn and bramble
   About the hollow ground
   The primroses are found.

And there's the windflower chilly
   With all the winds at play,
And there's the Lenten lily
   That has not long to stay
   And dies on Easter day.

And since till girls go maying
   You find the primrose still,
And find the windflower playing
   With every wind at will,
   But not the daffodil.

Bring baskets now, and sally
   Upon the spring's array,
And bear from hill and valley
   The daffodil away
   That dies on Easter day.

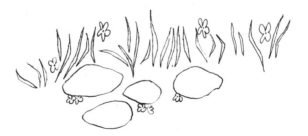

EASTER

BY EDWIN L. SABIN

The barrier stone has rolled away,
   And loud the angels sing;
The Christ comes forth this blessed day
   To reign, a deathless King.
For shall we not believe He lives
   Through such awakening?
Behold, how God each April gives
   The miracle of Spring.

AT EASTER TIME

BY LAURA E. RICHARDS

The little flowers came through the ground,
 At Easter time, at Easter time:
They raised their heads and looked around,
 At happy Easter time.
And every pretty bud did say,
 "Good people, bless this holy day,
For Christ is risen, the angels say
 At happy Easter time!"

The pure white lily raised its cup
 At Easter time, at Easter time:
The crocus to the sky looked up
 At happy Easter time.
"We'll hear the song of Heaven!" they say,
 "Its glory shines on us today.
Oh! may it shine on us alway.
 At holy Easter time!"

'Twas long and long and long ago,
 That Easter time, that Easter time:
But still the pure white lilies blow
 At happy Easter time.
And still each little flower doth say
 "Good Christians, bless this holy day,
For Christ is risen, the angels say
 At blessed Easter time!"

EASTER WEEK

BY CHARLES KINGSLEY

See the land, her Easter keeping,
  Rises as her Maker rose.
Seeds, so long in darkness sleeping,
  Burst at last from winter snows.
Earth with heaven above rejoices,
  Fields and gardens hail the spring;
Shaughs and woodlands ring with voices,
  While the wild birds build and sing.

You, to whom your Maker granted
  Powers to those sweet birds unknown,
Use the craft by God implanted;
  Use the reason not your own.
Here, while heaven and earth rejoices,
  Each his Easter tribute bring—
Work of fingers, chant of voices,
  Like the birds who build and sing.

SHEEP AND LAMBS

BY KATHARINE TYNAN HINKSON

All in the April morning,
  April airs were abroad;
The sheep with their little lambs
  Pass'd me by on the road.

The sheep with their little lambs
  Pass'd me by on the road;
All in an April evening
  I thought on the Lamb of God.

The lambs were weary, and crying
  With a weak human cry,
I thought on the Lamb of God
  Going meekly to die.

Up in the blue, blue mountains
  Dewy pastures are sweet:
Rest for the little bodies,
  Rest for the little feet.

All in the April evening,
  April airs were abroad;
I saw the sheep with their lambs,
  And thought on the Lamb of God.

BALLAD OF TREES AND THE MASTER

BY SIDNEY LANIER

Into the woods my Master went,
Clean forspent, forspent.
Into the woods my Master came,
Forspent with love and shame.
But the olives they were not blind to Him,
The little gray leaves were kind to Him:
The thorn tree had a mind to Him
When into the woods He came.

Out of the woods my Master went,
And He was well content.
Out of the woods my Master came,
Content with death and shame.
When Death and Shame would woo Him last,
From under the trees they drew Him last:
'Twas on a tree they slew Him—last
When out the woods He came.

THE ORIGIN OF THE EASTER LILIES
UNKNOWN

Within the rich man's garden
　　Full many a flower was seen,
With crowns of gold and crimson
　　On cups of emerald green.

They brought the dead King hither
　　And every flower in bloom
Bowed down its head in sorrow
　　About the Saviour's tomb.

But see! the white winged angels
　　Have rolled the stone away,
And 'mid the flowers only
　　The white grave cerements lay.

Next day they sought to find them,
　　Lo! rising where they fell
Like the hand of an angel
　　Waved there—a lily's bell.

So pure, so white, so spotless,
　　It pointed in the air,
As if to tell newcomers
　　That He had risen there.

Born of His white robes fallen
　　Like white leaves folded up,
They found a scepter golden and small
　　Within each fragrant cup.

And so among the blossoms
　　Amidst the rich man's bowers,
Was born the Easter lily,
　　The angel of the flowers.

JOY

From *Humanitad*

BY OSCAR WILDE

Already the slim crocus stirs the snow,
And soon yon blanched fields will bloom again
With nodding cowslips for some lad to mow,
For with the first warm kisses of the rain
The winter's icy sorrow breaks to tears,
And the brown thrushes mate, and with bright eyes the rabbit peers.
From the dark warren where the fir cones lie,
And treads one snowdrop under foot, and runs
Over the mossy knoll, and blackbirds fly
Across our path at evening, and the suns
Stay longer with us; ah, how good to see
Grass-girdled Spring in all her joy of laughing greenery!

EASTER MORN
BY AILEEN FISHER

Group: Now everything is born again
all up and down the earth,
for it is Easter morn again—
the morning of rebirth.

Boy: The grass is turning green again,
with frosty winter over.

Girl: And dandelions are seen again,
and daffodils, and clover.

Boy: And all the roots and all the shoots
and all the seeds are stirring.

Girl: And in the trees, the willow trees,
sit pussy willows, purring.

Group: Now everything is new again
all up and down the land,
for Easter has come true again
and hillsides understand.

Boy: The wind is bright and warm again
in all the open places.

Girl: The meadow larks perform again.
And daisies show their faces.

Boy: And all the leaves on all the trees
are starting to unfold.

Girl: While, on the run, the Easter sun
shakes out its living gold.

Group: Now everything is bright again
all up and down the world.
The tendrils that were tight, again
are magically uncurled.

Boy: And voices start to sing again.

Girl: And eyes begin to see
the worth of everything again,
as Easter turns the key.

Boy: And mankind feels the pull again
of Something from above.

Girl: And everyone is full again
of faith, and hope, and love.

Group: And everyone is full again
of faith, and hope, and love.

EASTER STORIES

Even Unto the End of the World

Micah lived in Netophah, a little village about twenty miles from Jerusalem. His father was dead and he and his mother and ten year old sister were very poor. Micah could remember a time when he wasn't hungry, when his father was alive and provided for them. Now that he was twelve years old he ought to be taking his father's place, earning at least a little. But how could he? For Micah was lame, so lame that he could scarcely take a step without the crutch the village carpenter had made for him.

It was indeed a dreary little family that lived in their plaster walled cottage nearly two thousand years ago. Micah's mother mourned for his father, weeping long hours in the night, and he himself was not a happy person. He could not run and play with other boys, he could not work so that the family might have more to eat, and he spent a good deal of time just moping and being sorry for himself. And Miriam, his young sister, was so quiet and shy one never knew whether she was happy or not.

But it was she who gave Micah a new idea. She came in, one day, from the village well, set down the water jar she was carrying, and ran to her brother.

"Micah," she said eagerly, "there is much talk among the women of the man, Jesus of Nazareth. We have heard of him before, you know, and of His wonderful miracles, but we never quite believed them."

"Well," said Micah as Miriam paused, "is there any more reason to believe them now?"

"Yes!" The little girl's face was shining. "They say He has healed our neighbor's cousin who lives in Capernaum of a tormenting fever, and someone told of a man who was born blind and Jesus of Nazareth gave him his sight. Oh, Micah, if you could only get to Him, you might be healed of your lameness!"

"How can I get anywhere?" The boy looked down at his thin useless leg.

"But they say He is likely to be in Jerusalem over the Passover. If you started in plenty of time, if you left here tomorrow and walked only a little each day, with your crutch, I'm sure you could get there."

At first Micah brushed the idea aside, but he was very quiet the rest of that day and early the next morning he was up and full of eagerness.

"Oh, Micah!" whispered Miriam, "then you are going! How I wish I were a boy and could go with you!"

Their mother shook her head at first. "It is too far," she said. "And we know no one at all in Jerusalem."

"But, Mother," Miriam insisted. "Bethany is almost on the way and you know we have relatives there. If he could manage to get to Bethany they would give him food and let him rest awhile before going on to the city. And Mother, think what it would mean if his leg could be made whole and he wasn't lame any more!"

"I doubt very much if such a thing is possible, but then, per-haps if he wants to go—" The troubled lines in the mother's face smoothed out, and she smiled at Micah lovingly.

"I do want to go," said the boy. "Other people have been healed. If I can only find Him—Jesus of Nazareth———"

"And you can! I know you can!" Miriam interrupted him with a hug. Then she ran off to wrap a little food in a clean napkin for him to take with him, a few figs, some hard bread, denying herself that he might have more.

Miriam's hope and eagerness fired them both, and Mother sped the boy on his way with a brave, "God be with you, my son. And may you be in time to find that good man of Nazareth while He is still in Jerusalem."

It was slow and difficult going, however. Any use of his lame leg gave Micah much pain. His crutch was too low for him and made his back and shoulder ache miserably. Half a dozen times during the first day of his journey, he decided to give the whole thing up, turn back and go home. What was the use anyway? It was four years since he had had the crippling disease that had left him partly paralyzed. Probably the wonder-worker of Nazareth was a fake and would not be able to help him.

But each time he had nearly given up some little thing had happened to renew his courage and spur him on. A woman had drawn some water for him at a well where it was too deep for him to get it for himself. A man with a donkey had offered to let him ride for a few miles. A child had smiled up at him in friendly fashion. "Where are you going?" the child asked.

"I want to find Jesus of Nazareth," he replied, new resolution entering into him as he spoke.

"Oh," said the child, slipping a hand in his free one. "I know Him. He was here once. I liked Him. I'll walk a little way with you if you want me to."

The following days were much the same. People were kind. Some gave him a bit of food. A shepherd allowed him to sleep near his fire on a cold hillside. And many times when he was asked where he was going and made the same answer, "I want to find Jesus of Nazareth," there would come a warm happy look into the questioner's face. "Yes, I know. I have seen Him," or, "He passed this way once, I talked with Him." Often that was all, but the lighted face spoke more than the words did.

Micah's desire to find Jesus of Nazareth grew keener with each mile, and hope became almost a surety that if he did find Him and ask for healing he would be made whole. Yet still the going was so slow and so painful.

He turned aside from the straight way north and came at last to the town of Bethany. Every inch of his body ached with weari-

ness. The crutch had chafed the skin under his arm until it was raw. It seemed as if he could not take another step, but he forced himself on to the house of the relatives to whom his mother had directed him. When he found it he leaned against the door and drew a long breath before he rapped on it. If only he could rest for a little before going on to Jerusalem! If only he could have a real meal to stay his constant hunger! He knocked on the door, waited, then knocked again. No answer, and the sound had the hollow ring that echoes through an empty house.

At that moment a woman approached from a neighboring cottage. "No one's at home there," said she. "They've all gone to Jerusalem for the Passover. What do you want?"

"I want Jesus of Nazareth," said Micah. He was so tired that his voice trembled.

"Well, now, that's too bad." The woman's voice was friendly. "He was here last night, at the home of Lazarus and his sisters. You are just too late."

Tears of disappointment slipped out of the boy's eyes, and he turned his face away. "I—I do want to find Him and ask Him to heal my leg."

"You'd better hurry to Jerusalem then. Day after tomorrow is the Sabbath, you know. You can't walk so far on that day, and after that He will probably go back to Galilee."

Micah, struggling to get control of himself, said nothing, and after a moment the woman continued, "You can sleep in our house if you like and start early in the morning."

"Thank you," said Micah huskily, and limped after her.

She was very kind to him, gave him something to eat and a rug to sleep on, and the next morning he was awake at dawn ready to be on his way.

He had not realized how big Jerusalem was, nor how crowded. The narrow streets were full of people hurrying this way and that. Over and over again he stopped a likely looking stranger and asked, "Do you know where I can find Jesus of Nazareth?"

Most of them shrugged their shoulders; some said hastily, "How should I know?" as if the question frightened them. One, in the clothing of the Pharisees, laughed disagreeably, saying, "Ask the Romans who guard the prisoners. They should be able to tell you."

Micah drew back at this as though he had been struck. The man must have misunderstood him. Jesus of Nazareth under guard? That could not be! But it made him hesitate to ask others, and he joined a group of people who all seemed headed in the same direction.

Before long he found himself on the outskirts of the city. The crowd had increased. They talked to each other in low, troubled tones. There were women among them. After a while they stood still beside a road leading apparently beyond the city walls.

"They will pass by here," someone said.

Micah squirmed his way to the edge of the road and took his stand near a man with a kindly face.

"What are you here for?" the man said. "This is no place for a young lad."

"I am looking for Jesus of Nazareth," the boy replied. "I want him to heal my leg."

The man laughed mirthlessly, ending in a groan. "You are too late, my son. Here comes Jesus of Nazareth now. They are taking Him to Calvary to be crucified."

"*Crucified!*" cried Micah. "Why?"

He received no answer. The crowd was straining forward. Up the narrow road toward them marched Roman soldiers, and among them three figures bowed beneath the weight of the heavy crosses on which, as criminals, they would hang. The middle one staggered a little and fell. There was a pause while a big stalwart fellow was summoned from the crowd to bear the cross for Him. A woman ran forward with a linen cloth and wiped the streaming sweat from the fallen prisoner's face. As He stood up again He spoke to her and to the women near Him. Then He turned. For one long moment Micah looked into the face of Jesus of Nazareth. In that moment he forgot his aching, dragging leg, he forgot himself, he forgot everything. A great burning love welled up within him; he wanted nothing in heaven or earth but to be with Him forever. And then Jesus with a little smile—for him—turned away again.

The sad procession moved on. The crowd fell in behind them. With a smothered cry Micah plunged into the midst of them. He must get nearer to Jesus, he must be with Him, follow Him even to Calvary. He must! He must! People pushed and shoved; the boy's crutch was knocked out of his hand and he fell. He struggled desperately to get up, again and again, only to fall back. He screamed but no one noticed him. Trampling feet bruised and cut him. Someone's staff knocked against his head and he lost consciousness.

When Micah came to, he found himself in a strange house. A number of women were moving about. There was a sound of heartbroken sobbing. He was lying on a soft rug in the corner of a large room. One of the women approached him. Her eyes were red with weeping, her voice quiet and low as she asked, "Are you better now? Is there much pain?"

"Where am I? What happened after—after?" As the scene on the road to Calvary flooded back into his memory, he shuddered.

"You are in the house of—of friends of our Lord Jesus." Her voice caught in a sob, but she steadied her trembling lips and went on. "You must have fallen in the crowd and would have been trampled to death if one of us had not fought his way to you and brought you here. You have a bad gash in your head and were unconscious for some time." She bent and felt his forehead with a practiced hand.

Micah smiled up at her. "You are very kind. Who are you, lady?"

"I am Mary of Magdala, and now I am going to get you somewhat to eat." She moved away and returned soon with something warm and comforting to his hungry stomach. But it seemed to Micah that nothing could ever warm or comfort his hungry heart. Jesus of Nazareth was dead. They had crucified Him. Now he would never be able to find Him again, never be with Him even for a moment, never follow Him, never serve Him as he longed to do with every ounce of his being. He felt as if the world had dropped out from under his feet and there was nothing left.

It was a strange day; the Sabbath, so no one did anything, of course, except Mary of Magdala. She saw to it that he had what he needed, bathed his throbbing head, and changed the cloths on his bruises and open cuts. He ached and was sore all over but apparently no bones had been broken. Lying in his corner he watched the people who sat about and the occasional new ones who came and went. They talked very little and never before had Micah known such a sense of enveloping sadness. It was as if in the death of Jesus all their hopes had been lost, their whole lives turned into a despair as gray and bitter as ashes in a burnt-out fire. Strangely he felt as if he knew and understood their feelings because of that one moment in Jesus' presence. And one time when Mary was leaning over him he whispered, "I love Him, too." Mary's face shone for a moment, and she smiled at him through her tears.

The next day Micah was awakened by the sound of a door opening. The early morning sun flooded into the dimly lit room and with it, as if borne on the wings of joy, came Mary, *his* Mary as he now thought of her. Two other women and two men followed. Micah recognized them as friends of Jesus. Those who were in the house came running to meet them.

"He is not dead! He is risen!" Mary cried, in a voice shaken but ringing with gladness. "He has risen from the dead as He said He would! I have seen Him! I have seen the Master!"

There was a moment's hush, a profound stillness, but only for a moment. Then awed questions and radiant answers, exclamations of wonder, exultant words of prayer. Micah could see and feel heartbreak change into triumphant happiness, dead despair into living hope and joy too great for utterance.

The boy lay trembling in his corner, looking from shining face to shining face, from half-believing rapture to glorious acceptance. He did not fully understand, yet he knew that something tremendous had happened. The man Jesus of Nazareth, whom these people called Master and Lord, had come back from crucifixion and death and was alive again!

More and more people came in. Over and over, those who had gone at daybreak to the tomb repeated their story. The great rock sealing the grave had been rolled away. A bright angel sitting within had said to them, "Why seek ye the living among the dead? He is not here, He has risen." And Mary of Magdala had seen Him, Jesus Himself! He had called her by name!

Micah scarcely breathed as he listened, and the words that he heard seemed to burn themselves into his very soul.

Jesus had said, "I am the resurrection and the life. Because I live ye shall live also." He had said, "Fear not. Your sorrow shall be turned into joy." He had said, "I go before you into Galilee." He had said, "Behold, I shall be with you always, even unto the end of the world."

Micah left his corner and crept nearer and nearer the excited, joyful group. Now he touched Mary's sleeve with a shaking hand. "Could—could that possibly mean—even me?" he whispered.

Mary looked down at him, her eyes misted with tears of joy. "Yes, of course it means you too, if you love and trust Him. Just think *all* that it means! Even death doesn't matter any more. Only He matters, and He is alive and with us now and always— our Lord and Master, the Son of God."

Back in the village of Netophah, Micah's mother was waiting with an anxious heart. The boy had been gone now nearly two weeks. She should never have let him go so far, and he so lame, so young. And Jerusalem would be full of the Passover crowds.

He may have been injured. A dozen times a day she stood in the doorway watching for him.

"Don't worry, Mother," Miriam tried to comfort her. "It's a long way and Micah couldn't move very fast, you know." And then she added, to herself, "Going, he couldn't, but coming back—maybe he could even run!"

The two were standing together at the door when they noticed a group of the villagers coming toward them. Miriam spied him first, in the midst of them. "Mother!" she cried. "There's Micah now! Look! Look at him!"

And then the boy was in his mother's arms. She held him off for a moment, her eyes hungrily taking in his happy face, his slim young body, the joyful excitement that seemed to shine in him like a light.

"Micah," she said suddenly, "where is your crutch?"

The boy started as if he had been reminded of something he had completely forgotten. "My crutch?" he said. "Why—I don't know. I—I must have lost it somewhere." Then he looked down at his legs and laughed a gay, boyish laugh. He was standing squarely on his two feet; his left leg, limp and useless for so long, was strong and steady and whole.

"A miracle!" cried one of the neighbors in an awed voice, and others caught it up. "A miracle!" "A miracle!" "The Lord be praised!"

Miriam had been kneeling on the ground, feeling Micah's foot and ankle with loving fingers. Now she sprang up. "You've been with Jesus of Nazareth," she cried. "He has healed you! Oh, Micah, I am so glad! so glad! Tell us about it!"

"I have such wonderful things to tell you, Mother, Miriam, all of you. I forgot about my leg. Why, I've covered the distance from Jerusalem in two days and I'm not even tired! I haven't time to be, I've so much to think about! All life is different now!" He paused. His listeners hung upon his words without a sound.

Then he spoke again as if in a dream. "*He* must have done it—

Jesus of Nazareth, my Lord and Master. But I never asked Him to heal me. In that moment when I looked in His face I thought only of Him. And I loved Him! I love Him still—and I shall love Him always—even unto the end of the world!"

BY ELEANORE M. JEWETT

THE WHITE BLACKBIRD

"Oh, no, it cannot be," said all the creatures of the farmyard when the little wren told them what she had seen.

"Yes, yes, yes," said the little wren excitedly, "I flew and I fluttered along the hedges, and I saw it, just as I tell you."

"What did you see, oh, what did you see?" asked the foolish pigeons. They came to where the cock with the hens were standing, and they stretched out their necks to hear what was being said.

"Something too terrible to talk to foolish creatures about," said the cock as he went gloomily away.

"Too terrible, too terrible," said the robin redbreast mournfully, as she went hopping under the hedge.

Inside the house the Boy was standing, and he was looking into a cage. Within that cage was a bird he had caught. It was the most wonderful of all birds, for it was a white Blackbird. Now you might live a whole lifetime and never once see a white Blackbird. But this Boy had not only seen a white Blackbird—he had caught one.

He had put the white Blackbird into a cage, and he was going to keep it forever. He was a lonely Boy, this Boy who had caught the white Blackbird. His father he had never known. His mother was dead. He lived in the house of his grandmother, his mother's mother.

His father had once lived here, but that was at a time that the Boy had no remembrance of. Then, his mother being dead, his father and his grandmother had quarreled, and after that his father went away and was never heard of afterward. The Boy had no one to take him by the hand as other boys had. He used to tell his grandmother about seeing boys walking with their fathers, the boys holding their fathers' hands. But he had given up telling her about such sights, for she looked lonely when he spoke of them.

Now the Boy had a bird for his very own. That was a joy to him. The night before the Peep-show Man had been in the house. He came out carrying a lantern. He held the lantern into a bush. The light came upon a bird that was resting there. Dazzled by the light, the bird did not move, and the Peep-show Man put his hand upon the bird, caught it, and gave it to the Boy to keep. This was the white Blackbird.

The Boy put the bird into an empty cage. Now that he had something of his own, he would not be lonely nor sorry for himself when he saw such and such a boy walking with his father on the Easter Sunday that was coming. All day he watched the strange, white bird. And that night as he sat by the fire his eyes were upon the cage, and he watched the stirring of the white Blackbird within.

The robin redbreast that in the winter goes along under the hedge and the little wren that flies along the top of the hedge, were talking to each other. "Always, on Easter Sunday," said the wren, "I sing my first song of the year. My first song is for the risen Lord."

"And mine, too," said the robin redbreast. "But now we will not know that it is Easter Morning and that it is time to sing for the risen Lord. For the white Blackbird always showed itself to us in times before, and when it showed itself we knew it was Easter indeed."

"Oh, now we know what has happened," said the foolish pigeons. "The Boy has caught the white Blackbird that used to appear just before the sun was up every Easter Morning. He has brought the white Blackbird into the house and he has put it into a cage. It will not be able to show itself. Dear, dear, dear! We are truly sorry."

[171]

"The songs that the robin and the wren sing are not so very important," said the cock. "But think of the proclamation that I have made every Easter Morning. *Mok an o-ee Slaun*, 'The Son of the Virgin is safe.' I made it when the white Blackbird showed himself. Now men will not know that they may be rejoiceful."

"I—" said the wren, looking around very bravely.

"The world will be the worse for not hearing my tidings," said the cock.

"I—" said the wren again.

"The wren is trying to say something, and no one will listen to her," said robin redbreast.

"Oh, by all means let the wren keep on talking," said the cock, and he went away.

"Tell us, tell us," said the pigeons.

"I," said the little wren, "will try to set the white Blackbird free."

"How, how—?" asked the foolish pigeons.

"I might fly into the house when no one is watching," said the wren. "I can really slip into and out of places without being seen. I might manage to open the door of the cage that the white Blackbird is in."

"Oh, it is terrible in the house," said the foolish pigeons. "We went in once, picking grains. The door was closed on us. It was dark in there. And we saw the terrible, green eyes of the cat watching us. It is terrible in the house." Then the pigeons flew away.

"I should be afraid to go in," said the robin redbreast, "now that they have mentioned the eyes of the cat."

"I *am* afraid," said the little wren. "And there is no one that would miss me if anything terrible befell me. I really am so afraid that I want to fly right away from this place."

But then, although her little heart was beating very fast, the wren flew up on the thatched porch. There was no one could see her there, so small and so brown she was. When darkness came outside she fluttered into the house. She hid in a corner of the dresser behind a little luster jug. She watched the cage that had the white Blackbird in it. She saw the door of the house closed and bolted for the night.

Oh, all in a fright and a flutter was the little brown wren as she hid in one of the houses of men. She saw the terrible cat sleeping by the hearth. She saw, when the fire burned low, how the cat rose and stretched herself and looked all around the house with her terrible eyes. The Boy and his grandmother had now gone up to bed.

The wren could still see by the light that blazed upon the hearth. The cat went up one step of the stairs; but only a step. For as the wren fluttered up and alighted on the top of the cage the cat heard the sound that she made, light and all as it was, and she turned back and looked at the cage, and the little wren knew that the cat saw her and would watch her.

There was a little catch on the door of the cage. The wren pulled at it with her beak. She said to the bird within, "O white messenger——"

"How shall I fly out of the house—tell me, tell me," said the white Blackbird.

"We will fly up the chimney, and away," said the little wren as she opened the door.

Before the darkness had quite gone a man came along the road that went by that house. He had on the clothes of a soldier. He stood and looked at the house as he came before it. His little boy was there. But he would not stay to see him. The memory of the quarrel that he had had with the woman who lived there, the boy's grandmother, came over him. His heart was made bitter by that memory, and he would not cross her threshold.

It was near daylight now. Out of the hedge came a thin, little song. It was the song of the wren, he knew, and he smiled as he listened to it. He heard another song, a song with joyous notes in it, the first song that the robin sings from the hedge tops. All the times before she has been going under the hedges without a song.

And then he heard the cock crow. Loudly, loudly, the cock cried *"Mok an o-ee Slaun, mok an o-ee Slaun,"* and the man remembered that this was Easter Morning. He did not go on now. He waited, and he stood looking at the house.

And then, upon the thatch of the porch he saw a strange bird—a strange, white bird. The man could not go on now. Only once in a lifetime might one see a white Blackbird. And this was the second time he had seen one. Once before, and on an Easter Morning too, he had seen a white Blackbird. He had come to this house. Some one was living in it then who was dead since. The girl who became the mother of his boy was living here. He had come for her to this house so that they might go out together and see the sun rising on Easter Morning. And when he had come before the house he had seen a strange bird on the thatch of the porch—he had seen the white Blackbird then as he saw it now.

He did not go.

Then out of the house came a little Boy. He held an empty cage in his hand. He looked all around. He saw the white Blackbird upon the porch, and he held his hands to the bird as if trying to draw it down to him again.

The man went to the Boy. And the Boy, knowing him, caught the hand that was held to him. The Boy drew the man within. There was a woman at the hearth. She turned and saw the man.

"And you are safe, my daughter's comrade?" said the woman as she drew the man to her. "And now the child will have his father to take him by the hand this Easter."

The Boy felt that he would never again be lonely. He heard the robin singing. He heard the wren singing. He heard the cock outside telling the world about the risen Lord. He saw the white Blackbird flying away.

BY PADRAIC COLUM

[175]

THE BOY WHO DISCOVERED THE SPRING

There came once a little Elf Boy to live on this earth, and he was so much pleased with it that he stayed, never caring to go back to his own world. I do not know where his own world was, or just how he came to leave it. Some thought that he was dropped by accident from some falling star, and some that he had flown away, thinking that he could fly back again whenever he chose, because he did not know that children always lose their wings when they come into this world. But no one knew certainly, as he never told any one; and, after all, it did not matter, since, as I have already said, he liked the earth so much that he did not care to leave it.

There was a Hermit who lived in the valley where the little Boy had first come, and, as he had a room in his house for a visitor, he took him in, and they grew to like each other so well that again the little Boy did not care to go away, nor did the Hermit care to have him. The Hermit had not always been a Hermit, but he had become a sorrowful man, and did not care to live where other people lived, or to share any of their pleasures. The reason he had become a sorrowful man was that his only child had died, and it seemed to him that there was nothing worth living for after that. So he moved to the lonely valley, and I suppose would have spent the rest of his life by himself, if it had not been for the little Elf Boy.

It was a very lovely valley, with great, green meadows that sloped down to a rippling brook, and in summer-time were full of red and white and yellow blossoms. Over the brook there hung green trees, whose roots made pleasant places to rest when one

was tired; and along the water's edge there grew blue flowers, while many little frogs and other live creatures played there. It was summer-time when the little Elf Boy came, and the flowers and the trees and the brook and the frogs made him very happy. I think that in the world from which he came they did not have such things: it was made chiefly of gold and silver and precious stones, instead of things that grow and blossom and keep one company. So the Elf Boy was very happy. He did not ask to go to play in the village over the hill, but was quite content with the meadows and the brook-side. The only thing that did not please him was that the old Hermit still remained sorrowful, thinking always of his child who had died; and this the Elf Boy did not understand, for in the world from which he came nothing ever died, and he thought it strange that if the Hermit's child had died he did not patiently wait for him to come back again.

So the summer went merrily on, and the Elf Boy learned to know the names of all the flowers in the meadow, and to love them dearly. He also became so well acquainted with the birds that they would come to him for crumbs, and sit on the branches close by to sing to him; the frogs would do the same thing, and although the Elf Boy did not think their voices as sweet as those of the birds, he was too polite to let them know it.

But when September came, there began to be a sad change. The first thing the Elf Boy noticed was that the birds began to disappear from the meadows. When he complained of this, the Hermit told him they had gone to make their visit to the Southland, and would come back again; and this he easily believed. But as time went on, and the air became more and more still as the last of them took their flight, he began to lose heart.

What was worse, at the same time the flowers began to disappear from the meadows. They were dead, the Hermit said, and in this way the Elf Boy learned what that meant. At first others came to take their places, and he tried to learn to like the flowers of autumn as well as those which he had known first. But as these faded and dropped off, none came after them. The mornings grew colder, and the leaves on the trees were changing in a strange way. When they grew red and yellow, instead of green, the Elf Boy thought it was a queer thing for them to put on different colors, and wondered how long it would last. But when they began to fall, he was very sad indeed. At last there came a day when every limb was bare, except for a few dried leaves at the top of one of the tallest trees. The Elf Boy was almost broken-hearted.

One morning he went out early, to see what new and dreadful thing had happened in the night, for it seemed now that every night took something beautiful out of the world. He made his way toward the brook, but when he reached the place where he usually heard it calling to him as it ran merrily over the stones, he could not hear a sound. He stopped and listened, but everything was wonderfully still. Then he ran as fast as his feet would carry him to the border of the brook. Sure enough, it had stopped running. It was covered with a hard sheet of ice.

The Elf Boy turned and went to the Hermit's house. By the time he had reached it, the tears were running down his cheeks.

"Why, what is the matter?" asked the Hermit.

"The brook is dead," said the Elf Boy.

"I think not," said the Hermit. "It is frozen over, but that will not hurt it. Be patient, and it will sing to you again."

"No," said the Elf Boy. "You told me that the birds would come back, and they have not come. You told me that the trees were not dead, but their leaves have every one gone, and I am sure they are. You told me that the flowers had seeds that did not die, but would make other flowers; but I can not find them, and the meadow is bare and dark. Even the grass is not green any more. It is a dead world. In the summer-time I did not see how you could be sorrowful; but now I do not see how any one can be happy."

The Hermit thought it would be of no use to try to explain anything more to the Elf Boy; so he said again, "Be patient," and tried to find some books in which he could teach the Boy to read, and make him forget the outside world.

The next time they went for a walk to the village over the hill, the Elf Boy was very curious to see whether the same thing had happened there that had happened in their valley. Of course it had: the trees there seemed dead, too, and the flowers were all gone from the door-yards. The Boy expected that every one in the village would now be as sorrowful as the Hermit, and he was very much surprised when he saw them looking as cheerful as ever. There were some boys playing on the street-corner, who seemed to be as happy as boys could be. One of them spoke to the Elf Boy, and he answered, "How can you play so happily, when such a dreadful thing has happened to the world?"

"Why, what has happened?"

"The flowers and trees are dead," said the Elf Boy, "and the birds are gone, and the brook is frozen, and the meadow is bare and gray. And it is so on this side of the hill also."

Then the boys in the street laughed merrily, and did not answer the Elf Boy, for they remembered that he was a stranger in the world, and supposed he would not understand if they should try to talk to him. And he went on through the village, not daring to speak to any others, but all the time wondering that the people could still be so happy.

As the winter came on, the Hermit taught him many things from the books in his house, and the Elf Boy grew interested in them and was not always sad. When the snow came he found ways to play in it, and even saw that the meadow was beautiful again, though in a different way from what it had been in summer. Yet still he could not think the world by any means so pleasant a place as it had been in the time of flowers and birds; and if it were not that he had become very fond of the Hermit, who was now the only friend he could remember, he would have wished to go back to the world from which he had come. It seemed to him now that the Hermit must miss him very much if he should go away, since they two were the only people who seemed really to understand how sorrowful a place the earth is.

So the weeks went by. One day in March, as he and the Hermit sat at their books, drops of water began to fall from the eaves of the roof, and they saw that the snow was melting in the sunshine.

"Do you want to take a little walk down toward the brook?" asked the Hermit. "I should not wonder if I could prove to you today that it has not forgotten how to talk to you."

"Yes," said the Elf Boy, though he did not think the Hermit could be right. It was months since he had cared to visit the brook, it made him so sad to find it still and cold.

When they reached the foot of the hillside the sheet of ice was still there, as he had expected.

"Never mind," said the Hermit. "Come out on the ice with me, and put down your ear and listen."

So the Elf Boy put down his ear and listened; and he heard, as plainly as though there were no ice between, the voice of the brook gurgling in the bottom of its bed. He clapped his hands for joy.

"It is waking up, you see," said the Hermit. "Other things will waken too, if you will be patient."

The Elf Boy did not know quite what to think, but he waited day after day with his eyes and ears wide open to see if anything else might happen; and wonderful things did happen all the time. The brook sang more and more distinctly, and at last broke through its cold coverlet and went dancing along in full sight. One morning, while the snow was still around the house, the Elf Boy heard a chirping sound, and, looking from his window, saw a red robin outside asking for his breakfast.

"Why," cried the Boy, "have you really come back again?"

"Certainly," said the robin, "don't you know it is almost spring?"

But the Elf Boy did not understand what he said.

There was a pussy-willow growing by the brook, and the Boy's next discovery was that hundreds of little gray buds were coming out. He watched them grow bigger from day to day, and while he was doing this the snow was melting away in great patches where the sun shone warmest on the meadow, and the blades of grass that came up into the daylight were greener than anything the Elf Boy had ever seen.

Then the pink buds came on the maple trees, and unfolded day by day. And the fruit trees in the Hermit's orchard were as white with blossoms as they had lately been with snow.

"Not a single tree is dead," said the Elf Boy.

Last of all came the wild flowers—blue and white violets near the brook, dandelions around the house, and, a little later, yellow buttercups all over the meadow. Slowly but steadily the world was made over, until it glowed with white and green and gold.

The Elf Boy was wild with joy. One by one his old friends came back, and he could not bear to stay in the house for many minutes from morning to night. Now he knew what the wise Hermit had meant by saying, "Be patient;" and he began to wonder again that the Hermit could be sorrowful in so beautiful a world.

One morning the church bells in the village—whose ringing was the only sound that ever came from the village over the hill —rang so much longer and more joyfully than usual, that the Elf Boy asked the Hermit why they did so. The Hermit looked in one of his books, and answered:

"It is Easter Day. The village people celebrate it on one Sunday every spring."

"May we not go also?" asked the Elf Boy, and as it was the first time he had ever asked to go to the village, the Hermit could not refuse to take him.

The village was glowing with flowers. There were many fruit trees, and they, too, were in blossom. Every one who passed along the street seemed either to wear flowers or to carry them in his hand. The people were all entering the churchyard; and here the graves, which had looked so gray and cold when the Hermit and the Boy had last seen them, were beautiful with flowers that the village people had planted or had strewn over them for Easter.

The people all passed into the church. But the Hermit and the Elf Boy, who never went where there was a crowd, stayed outside where the humming-birds and bees were flying happily among the flowers. Suddenly there came from the church a burst of music. To the Elf Boy it seemed the most beautiful sound he had ever heard. He put his finger on his lip to show the Hermit that he wanted to listen. These were the words they sang:

"I am He that liveth, and was dead; and, behold, I am alive for evermore!"

The Boy took hold of the Hermit's hand and led him to the church door, that they might hear still better. He was very happy.

"Oh," he cried, "I do not believe that anything ever really dies."

The Hermit looked down at him and smiled. "Perhaps not," he said.

When the music began again, a strange thing happened. The Hermit sang the Easter song with the others. It was the first time he had sung for many years.

BY RAYMOND MACDONALD ALDEN

WHY THE IVY IS ALWAYS GREEN

There were once two small plants that grew on the edge of a rough, red ditch. One of them was an ivy plant and the other a tiny fig tree.

It was early in the morning when they first awoke and looked around to see how they liked the world.

"I think it is an ugly old world," said the young fig tree. "I see only a rough, red ditch with dirty water flowing below."

"Oh, it is a beautiful world," replied the ivy vine. "I see clouds floating on high, and sunshine, and such lovely trees and flowers growing over on the other side of the ditch! Let us try to make this side beautiful, too. I will cover the rough, red places with pretty, green leaves, and you can decorate with your wonderful pink blossoms. Come, let us try."

"No," said the small fig tree, "I would not waste my time trying to make this ugly old place beautiful.

"Now if, like my mother, I could have grown in the soft, rich earth of the garden, I would have tried to do something, but here there is no use."

So, from day to day, the little fig tree grumbled. Nothing pleased her. If the sun shone she said it was too hot; if the rain fell she said it was too wet; and if the wind blew she said it was too cold.

But with the little ivy vine it was very different, and she was as happy as a lark from early morning until night.

"Whether the sun shines or whether the rain falls, it is God's will," said the little vine, "and I am well pleased. I shall do all I can to make my side of this ditch beautiful, and I shall begin today."

And so she did. Though she lived only on the edge of the red ditch, she spread out her leaves day by day, running here and there and yonder, hiding this red spot and that red spot, until by and by nothing could be seen but the beautiful green leaves of the ivy, and she did not stop until every ugly spot was hidden by her graceful garlands.

"Oh, it is beautiful, beautiful, now," cried the ivy, "only look!"

"Yes," said the fig tree, crossly, "but no one sees it. What are you going to do now? Dry up, I suppose, since you can never cross the ditch."

"Oh, but I shall cross the ditch," said the ivy vine. "I shall keep on trying until I do. There is so much on the other side I can do to help make the earth-world beautiful. Surely there is a way to cross."

So she ran out little tendrils, reaching here and there, searching everywhere for a way to cross the ditch. And at last, by climbing down to the edge of the muddy water, she reached a rock half way across, where she stopped for a moment to rest and wonder what next to do.

"You'll never get across," laughed the fig tree. "I told you so! You might as well make up your mind to dry up and stop trying."

"I shall never stop trying," called back the ivy vine. "There is a way to cross all ditches, and I shall cross this one. Wait and see."

"Bravo, my pretty one!" said the voice of the old oak tree close by. "Cling to my roots there. I am old and worn, but it is a joy to help one like you; reach out, and I will pull you up."

So with one huge stretch the ivy vine clung tightly to the twisted roots of the old oak and was soon laughing merrily on the other side.

"Dear me, but you are a brave little vine," said the old oak. "I have been watching you across the ditch all these months, and you have changed its ugly, red banks into a real thing of beauty.

"Now there was a time, once, when flowers and grass grew

there, and ferns fringed the edge of the brook, and it was beautiful indeed. Every fall I shook armfuls of crimson and yellow leaves upon the bank, but that was long ago, before the great forest fire which robbed me of my limbs and left me old and worn.

"What a joy it would be to me if only I might have my branches decked in leaves one more time—especially do I long for this in the glad springtime, when trees and flowers are robing themselves for the joyous Easter Day.

"Sad, indeed, it is to me, to know that I shall be clothed no more in a fresh dress of delicate green, like your own pretty leaves, dear Ivy."

"But you shall," said the ivy vine, clapping her hands; "you have helped me cross the ditch today, and I mean to give you an Easter dress. Watch me."

Now vines had never climbed high before this. They had only run along the ground and down the hill, and over walls, but this little ivy vine wrapped her delicate arms around the rough bark of the old oak and began to climb her first tree.

She pulled and stretched, and stretched and pulled, until little by little, up, up, higher and higher she went, leaving a trail of rich, green leaves behind her. It was a lovely sight.

"See!" she called to the old oak. "I am bringing you a most beautiful Easter dress. How do you like it?"

"Beautiful, beautiful!" laughed the old oak. "You make me feel young again. But what will you do when you reach my branches?"

"Why, I shall keep on climbing," replied the ivy vine. "When I give a dress at all, it must be a whole dress, don't you know? I shall not stop until I have covered every branch, as I did the bare spots on the ditch."

And so she did. Every day she climbed a little higher, until by and by every limb on the great, old oak was completely hidden by the beautiful leaves of the ivy. The old oak laughed in delight as she looked on her beautiful Easter dress of fresh, rich green.

Now the queen of the fairies, who was always on the watch for beautiful deeds, stood under the old oak on Easter Day and wondered at the beautiful sight. It made her glad to see the joy of the old oak in her new dress, and of course she knew who had given it.

So, turning with a smile to the ivy vine, she said, "Because you have tried to make others happy and to make the earth beautiful, your leaves shall never fade. Forever and forever they shall stay beautiful and green. Cold shall not hurt them nor summer's heat destroy them, and wherever you go you shall gladden the hearts of men with your freshness and beauty."

Very happy, indeed, did these words make the pretty ivy vine, and ever since she has been climbing over the earth-world, hunting bare places to make more beautiful.

Stone walls and churches and houses—no place seems too high for her to climb, and never does she weary in making fresh Easter dresses for the trees that are old and worn and cannot make them for themselves.

BY MADGE BIGHAM

CANDLES AT MIDNIGHT

Now that he was ten, Costas Papadopoulos remembered very little about that long-ago time when he was only five. He had little in common with the small boy who thought he was hungry if dinner was ten minutes late and who thought that soldiers were only for parades. But in spite of all Costas had learned about hunger and enemy soldiers during the last five years in Athens, there was one thing he did remember very clearly and very often. He could never forget the promises of the night before Easter, 1940.

"Next year you will be old enough to go," his father had promised him, speaking loudly because of the clanging of all the church bells of Athens. "It is enough this year for you to come up here on our flat roof at midnight to watch."

"And shall I have fireworks to set off?" Costas had asked. His eyes had sparkled at the red, green, and gold of the Roman candles and rockets hissing and popping from Mt. Lycabettus and other hills about Athens.

"We shall stand together on the highest rock of Mt. Lycabettus to fire our rockets," Kyrios Papadopoulos had promised his son.

"And shall I have a candle to carry?" Costas had asked. His eyes danced from one place to another, as people at all churches in Athens were obeying the midnight bells and lighting their Easter candles. His eyes raised again to Mt. Lycabettus where the bell of St. George's chapel was ringing in triumph. The top of the mountain was blossoming in tiny golden flames as lights were passed from one candle to another. "Shall I have a long, white candle to carry from the top of Mt. Lycabettus?"

"Of course you will!" his mother had promised. "And you will shield it with your hand so carefully that it will stay lighted all the time that you walk the winding path down the mountain and through the streets home. That will bring you good luck all the year."

Four Easters had passed since then, but there had been no midnight fireworks nor long, white candles for Costas. The spring when Costas was six, his father had been in the Greek army fighting in the mountains. The Easters when he was seven and eight and nine, there had been conquering soldiers in Athens, insisting that each Greek be in his own house early every evening.

Now that Costas was ten, beautiful Athens was free again. Often during that sunny week before Easter, 1945, Costas had climbed the twisting stairway to his roof to get a better look at Mt. Lycabettus. At almost any time, he could see the tiny figures of people toiling up the hill to say their Holy Week prayers in the gleaming, white-washed chapel of St. George at the summit.

"You are old enough to go alone now, Costas," his father said to him on the day before Easter.

"Yes, Father!" The boy understood why his father could not go with him. It had been four years now that Kyrios Papadopoulos had been out of the army and walking painfully with a cane. The long climb up Mt. Lycabettus would be hard for him at any time —quite impossible as part of the gay Easter crowd.

"I will watch from the roof," smiled the father. "Point your rockets over this house. Then I will know which are yours."

"All right," grinned Costas, who could feel the fireworks in his fingers already. "And the long, white candle—I will carry it carefully all the way down the mountain and through the streets. I will climb up to our roof and give it to you still burning."

"You can try," smiled his mother.

"I *will* do it!" said Costas. "And bring you good luck for a whole long year."

"I am sorry not to have more money for fireworks and candles

[190]

for you." Kyrios Papadopoulos opened his thin pocketbook and slowly counted out some worn paper money. "Two hundred drachmas is all we can possibly spare. That would have been plenty before the war. Prices are higher now. I hope it will be enough."

"You need spend nothing for Easter eggs." His mother pointed at the basket of blood-red eggs on the table. "You can carry two in your pocket. When the bells ring at midnight, you will want to crack eggs with the other boys."

"I will go to the market now to buy the candle and the fireworks." Costas was out the door and racing down the narrow street toward the wide streets, beyond which lay the market place. Not far from his own house, he saw a man with a pushcart, selling candles.

"How much?" asked Costas.

"Fifty drachmas for the short brown ones. Two hundred drachmas for the long white ones," droned the candle-seller.

"But the short ones would not burn all the way down Mt. Lycabettus!" wailed Costas.

"The long ones will—only two hundred drachmas," droned the candle-seller. His eyes were already on a woman who looked as though she had more money.

"But then there would not be anything left for buying fireworks!" groaned Costas.

The candle-seller shrugged his shoulders. He turned toward the young woman, who held out money for three long white candles.

Costas went slowly on. Perhaps if he went on toward the market streets, candles would be cheaper. He passed a man standing on the sidewalk holding a tray of fireworks.

"How much?" asked Costas.

"Fifty drachmas." The man pointed at some puny little firecrackers. "One hundred drachmas. One hundred and fifty. Two hundred." He pointed to fireworks that grew bigger with the bigger prices. The one for two hundred was a beauty.

Costas shuffled slowly on toward the market place near the foot of the ancient Acropolis. Some days he loved to gaze dreamily at the stately Parthenon and the dainty Temple of Victory outlined against the sky. But today he was wondering merely if, where there were many salesmen, prices would be lower.

"How much?" he asked of candle salesmen with trays, with baskets, with pushcarts.

"Fifty for the short brown ones. Two hundred for the long white ones." The answer was always the same.

"How much?" he asked of men selling candles in the sidewalk kiosks or in the stores.

"Fifty for the short brown candles. Two hundred for the long white ones."

"How much?" Costas asked of the candle salesmen sitting at

tables beside the doors of churches.

"Fifty for the short brown ones. Two hundred for the long white ones."

Costas soon found it did no good to explain to the candle-sellers that he had only two hundred drachmas with which he must buy at least one rocket and a long white candle that would burn all the time that it took him to climb down Mt. Lycabettus, walk to his own house, and mount the stairs to his father's roof. The candle salesmen were always busy selling to someone whose drachmas did not have to spread so far. Costas looked enviously at grimy bootblacks and ragged water-boys who could earn money of their own to spend.

It was nearly dark when Costas carried a long, slim, newspaper-wrapped parcel into the one big room that was home for himself and his parents. Tired, he flung himself onto the bed, under the picture of his father in uniform, while his mother put the plain supper on the table. This was the last of the fast-day meals. At midnight, with the cracking of the blood-red Easter eggs, the feasting would begin. Tomorrow there would be roast lamb.

"Did you find the candle and fireworks?" asked his mother.

"Yes." But Costas did not offer to unroll his long, slim parcel.

"I wish I could climb Mt. Lycabettus with you tonight," said his mother, laying crunchy chunks of dark brown bread at each place. "But you know how hard it is for your father to be lame. I will watch with him from the roof. I will wait with him for you to come up the stairs to us with the last flickers of your tall, white Easter candle."

"Yes, Mother." Costas fingered the parcel. He started to say something. Just then his mother whisked out into the courtyard to draw cool water for the table. Costas said nothing.

Supper over, he rested a while, his paper parcel clutched tightly.

"Ten o'clock," called his father. "It's time to get ready to start up Mt. Lycabettus. You will want plenty of time to go into the chapel before midnight."

Costas rubbed sleepy eyes. He staggered out into the courtyard where, with a gourd, he dipped water from a big barrel to pour over his head, his hands, his feet. It was already warm enough to begin saving wear on shoes.

Costas went back to the table in the one big room. He chose two large blood-red eggs to stuff in his trouser pockets. He lifted the long paper parcel carefully and started for the door.

"We will be up on the roof when the bells begin to ring at midnight," promised his mother. "We will be watching the fireworks and the candles till you come climbing up the stairs with your burning candle."

Costas stood in the doorway as though there was something he wanted to say. He turned his long parcel slowly in his hand. He cleared his throat—but all that came was, "Good-by, Father. Good-by, Mother." He turned and went out alone into the night.

Costas had climbed Mt. Lycabettus often in the daytime, but never before in the middle of the night. He dodged through one dark, narrow street after another until one street ended in a long flight of stone steps. Then a turn to the left and he was on the broad road which hairpinned through the pines for the lower stretches of the trail up the mountainside.

Then he turned off onto the path that zigzagged back and forth between the giant cactus plants, ascending little by little the steep sides of Lycabettus.

He could not leap ahead at his own speed because the path was filled with people climbing slowly, up and up. This gave more time to look down at the twinkling lights of the sprawling city. Where the loop made broad spots in the trail, salesmen of candles and fireworks had set up their little tables. Costas stopped by one and watched a bent little woman buy a short brown candle. He stopped by the next one and saw a well-dressed man count out two hundred drachmas for a tall white candle. He noticed that the fireworks were practically all sold out. He shifted his paper parcel to his other hand and climbed on up the looping path.

At the top of the mountain, he wriggled through the crowd around the door of the chapel. Inside there were soft lights burning before sacred pictures. The long-haired priest in his black robes was chanting with the choir while people moved quietly in and out of the chapel. Everywhere was the thick fragrance of incense.

Costas did not linger long. He wanted to be on top of the highest point of Mt. Lycabettus when the midnight bells should announce that Easter had arrived. He went outside and climbed the high wall that edged the enclosure east of the chapel. He could look down at the lights of all Athens and Piraeus. He could see even the twinkle of the big lanterns on fishermen's boats out in the harbor.

Mt. Hymettus rose dark behind him. Gleaming golden over the city were the ancient temples of the Acropolis, now bathed in floodlights in honor of Holy Week. Above him, the stars seemed almost close enough to touch.

Far below, the deep bell of the great Metropolitan Church rang out clearly. It was midnight. All over the city, bells sprang to life. A joyous clanging rose from all the churches, celebrating at once the Resurrection of their Lord and the new freedom of their country. So thrilled was Costas with the triumphant chorus of bells that he quite forgot to break his blood-red eggs on those of the boys standing near him. It was only the snapping and hissing of fireworks and the lighting of candles that reminded him that he, too, had a part in the celebration.

He discarded the newspaper wrapping and stood looking at his treasures—a long and beautiful rocket and a short brown candle. He looked in shame at the little candle made of the cheap dark tallow which burned so quickly.

"If I do not light it until I am almost home, they will never know," he tried to comfort himself. But the plan that had seemed all right in the market place seemed all too shabby under the stars, with the bells ringing joyously all about him, and the people sing-

[195]

ing with the priest the praises of the Risen Lord.

Fireworks were going off on every side, with people dodging them and laughing excitedly. Children were cracking eggs together, each trying to prove his the stronger egg. In an attempt to forget the smallness of his brown candle, Costas raised his rocket high over his head. He lighted a match that sputtered and went out. He struck a second match. He almost touched it to the rocket —but paused.

All around the people were lighting their tall white candles for the march home. As long as the rocket was unspent, there was still a chance to change his mind. He listened to the bells of triumph. He heard the people chanting, "Christ is risen. He is risen indeed."

Costas held the rocket high over his head. In a small voice that could scarcely be heard for the shouting about him, he called, "Rocket for sale. Skyrocket for sale. Two hundred drachmas." He waited and listened.

"I'll take it," said a voice close by. "I tried to buy some for my little Yiannis on the way here, but they were all sold."

Costas clung to his beautiful rocket for a moment. Then he handed it over, lingeringly, to the tall man who counted out four fifty-drachma notes.

"Would you mind," asked Costas in a tight, thin voice, "letting me stand nearby while Yiannis sets off the rocket?"

The rocket sputtered and sailed high over the heads of the crowd. As it flickered out, Costas' eyes were drawn by candle processions around other churches far below in the city. Then, grasping his two hundred drachmas in his hand, Costas wriggled his way through the crowd to the table by the chapel door where candles were sold.

"A long white candle," called Costas, laying down the four crumpled fifty-drachma notes with a glad flourish.

The candle-seller picked from the tray a candle that was truly beautiful in its tall, slim whiteness. The black-robed priest himself, smiling through his curly black beard, stooped to light

Costas' candle. From the white candle, Costas lighted his short brown one. He pushed his way into the little chapel and placed a small candle before a picture of the Virgin Mary and the baby Jesus.

Then, proudly, Costas joined the happy throng that was chanting its way down the mountainside, each person carrying a lighted candle.

"Christ is risen!" they greeted each other.

"He is risen indeed!" was the answer.

Costas did not care if the procession was slow. Wasn't his the longest, whitest candle ever carried by a boy on an Easter midnight? It would surely burn for every stately step down the mountainside, and for the quick walk through the narrow dark streets to his own home.

Singing and carrying his candle high, Costas pushed open his courtyard gate. One inch of candle left! Singing louder, he climbed the winding iron stairs to the roof. Three-quarters of an inch of candle left! The flame breathed hotly on his fingers as he crossed the roof to where his father sat. Half an inch of burning candle he thrust into his father's waiting hands.

"Christ is risen!" greeted Costas.

"He is risen indeed!" answered his parents.

BY ALICE GEER KELSEY

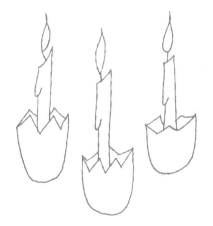

THE LOVELIEST ROSE IN THE WORLD

Once there reigned a queen, in whose garden were found the most glorious flowers at all seasons and from all the lands of the world. But more than all others she loved the roses, and she had many kinds, from the wild dog rose with its apple-scented green leaves to the most splendid, large, crimson roses. They grew against the garden walls, wound themselves around the pillars and window frames, and crept through the windows into the rooms, and all along the ceilings in the halls. And the roses were of many colors, and of every fragrance and form.

But care and sorrow dwelt in those halls. The queen lay upon a sickbed, and the doctors said she must die.

"There is still one thing that can save her," said the wisest of them. "Bring her the loveliest rose in the world, the rose that is the symbol of the purest, the brightest love. If that is held before her eyes ere they close, she will not die."

Then old and young came from every side with roses, the loveliest that bloomed in each garden, but they were not of the right sort. The flower was to be plucked from the Garden of Love. But what rose in all that garden expressed the highest and purest love?

The poets sang of the loveliest rose in the world—of the love of maid and youth, and of the love of dying heroes.

"But they have not named the right flower," said the wise man. "They have not pointed out the place where it blooms in its splendor. It is not the rose that springs from the hearts of youthful lovers, though this rose will ever be fragrant in song. It is not the bloom that sprouts from the blood flowing from the breast of

the hero who dies for his country, though few deaths are sweeter than his, and no rose is redder than the blood that flows then. Nor is it the wondrous flower to which man devotes many a sleepless night and much of his fresh life—the magic flower of silence."

"But I know where it blooms," said a happy mother, who came with her pretty child to the bedside of the dying queen. "I know where the loveliest rose of love may be found. It springs in the blooming cheeks of my sweet child, when, waking from sleep, he opens his eyes and smiles tenderly at me."

"Lovely is this rose, but there is one that is lovelier still," said the wise man.

"I have seen the loveliest, purest rose that blooms," said a woman. "I saw it on the cheeks of the queen. She had taken off her golden crown. And in the long, dreary night she carried her sick child in her arms. She wept, kissed it, and prayed for her child."

"Holy and wonderful is the white rose of a mother's grief," answered the wise man, "but it is not the one we seek."

"The loveliest rose in the world I saw at the altar of the Lord," said the good Bishop. "The young maidens went to the Lord's table. Roses were blushing and pale roses shining on their fresh cheeks. A young girl stood there. She looked with all the love and purity of her spirit up to heaven. That was the expression of the highest and purest love."

"May she be blessed," said the wise man, "but not one of you has yet named the loveliest rose in the world."

Then there came into the room a child, the queen's little son.

"Mother," cried the boy, "only hear what I have read!"

And the child sat by her bedside and read from the Book of Him who suffered death upon the cross to save men, and even those who were not yet born. "Greater love there is not."

And a rosy glow spread over the cheeks of the queen, and her eyes gleamed, for she saw that from the leaves of the Book there bloomed the loveliest rose, that sprang from the blood of Christ shed on the cross.

"I see it!" she said. "He who beholds this, the loveliest rose on earth, shall never die."

BY HANS CHRISTIAN ANDERSEN

"I think," said Gull, "I really think we've had enough of winter."

The birds were sitting on a long branch of an oak that looked over some gardens where children played and people walked.

"But *is* there anything else?" said Starling, looking about him, for gray skies and thin black branches were all that he could see.

"There's always spring somewhere!" cried Robin.

"But why doesn't spring come to us? Doesn't it know how long we've been waiting?" Blackbird spoke solemnly.

"Something in me wants to sing," sighed Thrush, "but it can't."

"Oh! Oh! Oh!" fairly shouted Sparrow in his eagerness. "It's no use wondering when spring will come. Spring never left us, but is working in the earth and the trees, in our hearts too, and has been ever since the golden autumn."

"What an odd idea!" Blackbird turned to Sparrow. "Spring is sun and warmth and things growing—and there's little of that now." He shivered, looking at the gray sky.

"Of course there is," said Sparrow, "and if you'd look for spring you'd find it."

"Sparrow always was a chatterer," Starling said to Thrush very quietly. "He rather likes to hear himself talk."

"Perhaps Sparrow is right," Robin put in. "Why don't we have a look for spring and see if we can find any of its touches? It would be much better than all this wondering."

"We would have to fly very high and very wide to find anything at all," Thrush said.

"Well, I can do both." Gull spoke suddenly. Gull always did seize any opportunity to fly.

"And I can do neither—very well," Sparrow said cheerfully, "so I'll stop in the gardens, for I don't have to look for spring— I know it's here!"

So the birds agreed to go in search of spring for a day and a night and then return to the oak's long branch to tell each other what they had found.

There was a flutter of wings. Gull rose swiftly from the branch and soared off. The others watched him—not circling, not lighting on the wind as he loved to do, but soaring. Then, turning east, he flew straight as the longing that had lifted him drew him on.

"He's going toward the sun!" the birds cried.

One by one they rose from the branch. Robin flew south, Thrush west, the others wide and high, circling, wheeling, searching for a wind that would bear them, for a thought that would lead them. Only Sparrow remained on the branch, then he

dropped to the ground at the base of the tree and began pecking away at the earth, all the time singing to himself a song of his own rhyming to a tune of his own making.

A little boy came rolling his hoop down the walk; his hair blew in the wind, his eyes were shining. When he saw Sparrow he stopped and reaching into his pocket for a bit of bread tossed it to him. Sparrow took it and went on chattering while he nibbled.

"I know what you're saying." The little boy bent quite close to the sparrow. "You're saying spring is coming soon."

"Is coming?" chattered Sparrow. "Is here! Can't you see——"

But the little boy had gone on, calling to his nanny, "The sparrow says spring is here—and that's what I say, too!"

"Silly boy," Nanny said, "it's a cold gray winter day and——"

Sparrow couldn't hear the rest, nor did he want to very much; he simply went on chattering.

Gull flew east. Over the land, then over the tossing waves of the sea, all night he flew, stopping only to rest on the billowing water. Then into the dawn he flew, and when the gold sun came over the sea's green rim Gull saw that it was huge and warm and splendid and when it began to climb the sky it chose a high way.

"Hallo, O Sun!" cried Gull.

"Hallo, O Gull! Do you see my beams and how far I can throw them? Oh, I am strong and I grow stronger every day. This is my joy—to light the world!" And so saying, the sun mounted where Gull could not follow, but his warmth fell over Gull and Gull's heart was happy. He turned back. Straight he flew, west, west, west. There was a song within him that, though he might never sing it, bore him on, back to the green garden and the long dark branch of the oak.

Robin had flown south. He had flown toward a wood that he knew and, seeing the tall trees waving darkly, had dropped down out of the sky to the earth and hopping softly over the moss and dried leaves had made his way into the heart of the wood. Dusk came gently over the trees but Robin saw clearly, for distantly a pale star gleamed—a pale, frail bit of yellow that, instead of light, gave forth sweetness.

"O little delight, may I rest under your leaves?" Robin said very tenderly to the primrose.

"Yes, yes," she answered shyly.

Far into the night they whispered.

"How many of you are there?" asked Robin.

"I am the only one yet," the primrose answered.

"But to see you is to see a world of primroses," Robin nodded. "Think of the children who will love you with their eyes and hold you softly in their hands. Oh, what joys you bring!"

"I like to be loved," said the primrose.

In the morning Robin left her, soaring high through the trees, his heart nearly bursting within him—one tiny primrose, yet all of spring lay in her yellow petals. Over the land he sped to the oak's long branch, only stopping now and then to sing, sing, sing.

Thrush had flown to a garden he remembered singing in during the summer. "Then it was full of flowers and now—there'll be nothing, nothing," he thought sadly.

But as he neared the garden he saw a white carpet running over its edge and disappearing into the woodland, a lacy white carpet that danced in the evening wind. He dropped lower, then rose again. "It's snow," he shivered. "O my lovely garden, I must wait until summer has come again for you."

As he circled in the sky, he saw a little girl come from the house and, going toward the snow, stoop and gather some of it.

"One doesn't gather snow," Thrush thought quickly, and when the garden was alone again he dropped from the sky straight into the delicate lace of a mass of snowdrops. Something happened to Thrush then: the ice of winter that had held his heart let go and his heart poured from him in strains of song—pure as the white flowers, free as the evening, lovely and tender and clear.

In the house, the little girl heard and, standing very still, said to herself, for no one else was near, "I think a thrush is singing,

a thrush in the snowdrops! I wonder what he is saying."

The next morning Thrush returned to the oak, beating the air with impatient wings for joy of the message he bore.

Starling, when he had left the oak, had felt quite sure that spring was not to be found, so he merely flew a little distance, then settled into a comfortable tree and put his head under his wing. When he woke the next morning he went for a flight. Looking down on the land and seeing a river, he thought that he would follow it, but the river was moving swiftly and Starling had to fly fast to keep up with it.

"Odd, very odd," he muttered. "A river is usually a lazy thing. Why so fast, my friend?"

"Because I must hurry to reach the sea," the river called back. "So many streams are flowing into my waters, I must carry them into the sea and come back for more."

"But why is there so much water?"

The river was flowing on and could not answer, but a warm, soft pattering on Starling's wings said very clearly, "It's the spring rains, the fields are sodden with them, and all the little streams that water the earth are hurrying on to the sea."

Starling wheeled in his flight. This was a bit of news for him to tell the others.

Blackbird had flown over the land, rested in a hedgerow all night, and taken flight again on the sun's broad beam. Looking down from the sky he saw a new thing—he saw carpets of green running over the land, curling at the edges of brown fields where winter had lain overlong. New green, fresh green, flashing in the sun.

Dropping onto a branch to see the green more closely, he saw fat sticky buds upturned to the sky. He did not think, he did not move, but he put back his head and sang and sang. All the songs winter had locked within him poured forth—because the world was greening and there were buds on the trees.

Then he took wing.

The others had all reached the long branch of the oak and were sitting waiting for Blackbird. They were impatient to tell what they had seen, for each knew now what Sparrow had meant.

Gull spoke first. "I saw the sun mounting high, bringing light and warmth.

Then Robin: "I saw a pale star shining in the moss—a primrose —promise of delights in store."

Then Thrush: "I saw a carpet of snowdrops, and I sang and sang and sang."

Then Starling: "I saw rivers moving in haste to the sea and I felt the warm spring rains that had filled them to their brim."

Then Blackbird: "And I saw a tide of green rushing over the land. There was only one thing to do—that's why I was late getting back to you."

"What did you see, O Sparrow?" they all said to the little brown bird on the end of the branch.

"I didn't have to see, I knew," Sparrow replied quietly. "Do you think I could ever sing all winter if I had to go and find spring? I sing because I know that spring is here."

Sparrow dropped to the earth and began hopping around, singing the song of his own rhyming to the tune he had made himself, and as he sang the little boy rolled his hoop by and stopped and smiled. And an old gentleman nodded his head and tossed Sparrow a crumb. And a tiny girl clapped her hands. And a mother laughed with her baby, saying softly, "Little one, even the sparrow tells us spring is here."

The birds on the oak's long branch watched and listened. Then Gull murmured, "His is the only song that everyone understands, for even in winter he holds spring's secret in his heart."

BY ELIZABETH YATES

THE APPLE TREE

On winter days the children would put their faces close to the windowpane and say, "If only it were Spring!"

The window looked out on a little garden where in Summer flowers bloomed, but now it was covered with snow. The lilac bushes stood up bare and stiff, and even the wild clematis wore a gray beard like an old man and seemed bowed down with the cold. Only the lame robin, who had stayed behind when all his friends flew southward, would come and hop near the doorsill, ruffling up his feathers, to peck for crumbs, and the tracks of his feet were like tiny hands in the snow.

Then their mother would say, "Cheer up, children! The Winter is nearly over. Very soon Easter will be here, and then we shall have the birds and the flowers back again!"

The little sister asked, "When will it be really Spring? I want it to be Spring now!"

"When Easter comes," said their mother, "then it will be really Spring."

"Does Easter come only in the Spring?" the brother asked.

"Only in the Spring."

"And suppose Easter never came at all!"

"That cannot happen," their mother answered, smiling. "Easter always comes, every year."

So day by day, from the window, the little brother and sister looked out up the road to see if Easter was coming. Nearly all the people who went by they knew by sight, neighbors who would turn their heads and wave a hand to the children as they neared the gate; very few strangers passed by on the road, and none of these looked like Easter.

"Perhaps he will come tomorrow," the brother always said.

"I think he will be dressed all in white," the little sister said, "and wear a shiny thing on his head, like the lady at the circus."

"No," said her brother. "He won't be like that at all. He will ride a big black horse, and he will have a helmet and a golden belt, and carry a sword in his hand."

"I don't want him to have a sword," the little sister said. "I'm afraid of swords!"

"That's only because you're a girl. Swords can't hurt you if you aren't afraid of them." And be began to talk about the kind of horse that Easter would ride, very proud and coal black; it would lift its feet high at every step and have silver bells on the bridle.

The days passed, and presently the snow melted. The sun shone out, and little gray and pink buds showed on the tree branches. Now the lame robin was no longer as tame as he used to be; he came less often for crumbs and instead was always flitting about the bushes, looking for the best spot to build a nest in when his family came back.

The children could play out-of-doors now, but they always kept an eye on the road, in case Easter should pass by when they weren't looking, for it would be dreadful to have waited all these weeks and then miss seeing him. Who knew but he might ride by in the night and not stop at the cottage at all, especially if he were late and in a hurry?

And then one morning their mother stopped in her work to look at the calendar hanging on the wall by the fireplace, and exclaimed, "Why, how quickly the days do go by! Easter will be here before we know it!"

The children looked at each other and smiled.

"You see," the brother said. "He might come any minute now! We must be very careful!"

And so they always played in the front of the house, near the garden gate, where they could watch every one who went past.

One day it really felt like Spring. The sun seemed to shine

more brightly than ever before; the sky was blue and the air soft and warm. Even the grass looked greener than usual, and all the new leaves on the lilac bushes had unfolded during the night. In the long grass by the gate there were dandelions in blossom.

"Easter will surely come today!" said the brother. "Let's go a little way up the road, as far as the corner near the dead apple tree, and watch for him there."

So he took the little sister by the hand, and they went out through the gate and on to the road.

"I have saved a piece of bread in my pocket from breakfast," he told her. "So if you get hungry waiting we can sit down on the big stone by the tree and eat."

They set off, the little sister treading very carefully, for she was quite small, and where the path was stony she had to look first and see just where to put down each foot. Here and there along the edge of the road were tiny flowers, blue and white, and these the little sister wanted to stop and gather to give to Easter if they saw him. It took a long time; she gathered them quite short, with hardly any stalk, so that at every few steps they dropped from her hand and had to be picked up again. But the brother was very patient; he waited each time till she was ready to go on again, and in this way they came at last to the corner where the lane joined the highroad.

It was market day in the town, and a number of people were going by on the highway, but they all looked hurried or tired or busy; there was no face among them all that seemed like the face that Easter would have, except one girl, bare-headed, who was singing as she walked. She alone turned her head to smile at the children, but before they could speak to her she had gone on her way.

Nowhere, up or down the road, could they see anyone who looked at all like Easter. One man rode by on a horse, but he had no sword, and he looked very cross, so the children were afraid to step out and ask him. But presently a workman came along

with a bundle tied to a stick over his shoulder, and he stopped near the bank where the children were sitting to strike a light for his pipe.

"Could you tell me, please," the brother asked him, "whether Easter has gone by yet?"

"Why, no," said the workman slowly, staring at them. "Easter hasn't gone by yet, that I'm sure! I'm just going over to spend Easter day with my sister now. Over in the town where I've been working the folks don't set much store by Easter, but it's a holiday, so, thinks I, I'll pack up a few cakes for the little ones, and here I am. They'll be looking out for me surely! I wrote a letter to my sister a week ago, telling her. Just so sure as Easter comes, I said, I'll be there!"

"Then you know what Easter's like?" asked the brother.

"That I do!" said the workman. "Back in the country, when I was a boy, all the folks round about kept Easter, and we made a great feast every year. And that's why I'm going over to my sister's now, for the sake of old times, and to fetch the children a few cakes for the holiday. I'd give you some, and gladly, but it's a big family there and times are hard, so I was able to get only one apiece, all round, but that's better than nothing. Still, I slipped an apple or two in my pocket, coming along, and maybe you'd like them instead."

He pulled two big red apples out of his pocket and gave one to each of them.

"That's better than nothing," he said again as the children thanked him. "And now I must be getting on."

"Perhaps," said the brother, "you'll meet Easter on the road, if he hasn't gone by yet. Do you think you will?"

The workman laughed as if that were a great joke.

"Why, if I don't hurry up," he said, "I surely will! For it's all of twelve miles yet to my sister's house, and I just reckoned to get there by nightfall. So good-by, and a happy Easter to you both!"

[213]

He went off up the road, whistling, and walking very fast.

"Oh, dear," sighed the little sister, "I wish Easter would come quickly! I'm so tired of waiting!"

"We'll wait a little longer," said her brother, "and then we will go back and eat our lunch by the stone under the apple tree." For he too was beginning to feel rather tired of waiting there by the roadside. "You see, if there are so many people who want to keep Easter, that must make it hard for him to get about, and then it isn't his fault that he's late. Perhaps there is some one keeping him now, this very minute, and that's why he hasn't come. Of course, if he has a horse that would make it easier."

He thought of Easter, on a big black horse, riding through the villages, perhaps this very minute, and all the people stretching out their hands to stop him, and wanting him to stay with them. And the black horse tossing his head, to set all the silver bells ringing. It would be a fine thing to travel round with Easter, to walk by his side on the road and hold his horse whenever he dismounted. But the little sister thought of home, and a bowl of bread and milk, for she was getting sleepy.

The road was empty now; for a long while no one had passed up or down. But at last, very far in the distance, they could see someone moving. Under the hot, still rays of the sun, drawing the Spring moisture from the earth, the air seemed to tremble; distant objects, a line of poplar trees, the red-roofed farmhouse by the hill, even the surface of the road, blended and swam together, so that the brother, shading his eyes to gaze up the highway, could not be sure if what he saw were really a figure on a horse and the flash of gold and silver trappings, or just a cloud of dust gilded by the sunlight.

For a moment he thought he heard music, distant trumpets and the shouting of many voices, and then he knew that what he really heard was only the jingle of a sheep bell in the pasture and the crying of rooks on the plowed field, and that what he saw was no horse and rider, but only someone on foot, coming toward him along the road. And when the figure drew quite near he saw that it was a man, dressed in shabby clothes and walking slowly, as though he had come a long way on foot and was very weary. But when he saw the children he stopped to smile at them, and his smile was friendly.

"Are you waiting for someone?" he asked. "For I saw you from a long way off, looking out up the road."

"We are waiting for someone," said the brother, "but I'm afraid he can't be coming today, we have waited so long, and I think we will go back now and eat our bread under the tree, for my sister is getting tired."

"I'm tired, too," the stranger said, "so if I may I will come with you. Look, your little sister is nearly asleep!"

He picked the little sister up in his arms as he spoke. She was hot and tired and disappointed, and just getting ready to cry, but she put her head down on the man's shoulder and clung round his neck, for he held her like a person who is used to carrying little children. So they went, all three of them, back to the turn of the road and down the lane to where the apple tree grew.

It was quite an old tree, and for many years now it had not borne any blossom. Only a few twisted leaves came on it every Spring, and these soon withered and dropped. It was good to cut down for firewood, the farmer said, but the months passed and no one found the time to cut it, so it had been left standing there. The bare gnarled branches made a good enough shade in the Spring, and just beneath it was a big flat stone, comfortable to sit on, and near the stone a little trickling spring of water.

They sat down, the man with his back against the tree and the boy near him, and the little sister, who had forgotten her tiredness now, sat with her thumb in her mouth and looked at them both.

"I'm sorry I've only got a little piece of bread," said the brother, rather shyly, for he thought that perhaps the man was really a beggar, he was so poorly dressed, and in that case he might be quite hungry. "If I'd known I would have brought more."

"I expect it will be enough for all of us," the man said. And when he took the slice of bread from the brother's hand it certainly did seem larger than one had thought; he broke it into three pieces, and there was quite enough for all of them, as much as they wanted to eat. And it tasted wonderfully good, the brother thought; by far the best bread his mother had ever baked, but perhaps that was because he was so hungry.

They drank from the spring, and the man showed them how to make cups out of leaves, fastened with a thorn, that would hold the water. And after that he told them stories, jolly stories about the little reed that grew down in the ditch and wanted to be an oak tree, and about the king's son who had a dream and who threw his crown away and went out into the world and became a beggar. He seemed to be a very nice man indeed, and the children were glad they had met him.

"You must have come a very long way," said the brother presently. For he couldn't help noticing how dusty the man's feet were and that his clothes were quite worn.

"I have come a long way," the man said, "and I have still a long way to go."

"Is your home very far?"

"I have no home," he said. "Sometimes I find friends with whom I can stay for a little while, and they give me shelter. And there are others, goodhearted people, who think they want me, and ask me into their houses, but they don't really want me; they have business to look after and many things to do, and after a while they find I'm only a trouble to them, and out of place in their households, and they can't spare the time for me, and so I have to go."

"Do you never go back?" asked the brother.

"Yes, if someone dies or there is real trouble in the house and no one else to turn to, then they may remember and send for me, or they just leave the door ajar so I can come in."

"It must be a fine thing to travel all over the world," said the brother. He thought again of Easter and the tall black horse. "Wouldn't it be splendid to be a king, and then you would ride into the city and all the bells would ring and the people come out to meet you."

But the man didn't answer. Perhaps he hadn't heard, or was thinking of something else.

"Did you ever ride on a horse and have a sword?" the brother asked.

"I had a sword once," said the man, "but I gave it away."

"Weren't you sorry afterward?"

But again the man didn't answer; he was murmuring something, looking down on the earth at his feet; and the brother thought, Perhaps he really is sorry about the sword and doesn't like to speak of it. It was something one shouldn't have asked, and he didn't want to hurt the man's feelings. So he said aloud:

"Won't you tell us about some of the fine things you saw when you were traveling?"

The man looked up and smiled at them, and he put his hand inside the torn lining of his coat.

"This," he said, "is the most precious thing that I have found today, and I picked it up by the roadside."

He drew out his hand carefully; something very wonderful must be there, the boy thought, a tiny carved casket, or perhaps a jewel someone had dropped. But when he spread his fingers there was only a little brown bird on his hand, quite dead and limp, with its feathers ruffled, all dusty from lying in the road. The boy was disappointed; it wasn't at all what he expected to see, but the little sister reached out her hand.

"It's a bird!" she cried. "It's a dear little bird, and I don't want it to be dead!"

She stroked it with her tiny fingers as it lay on the man's hand, and there were tears in her eyes.

[217]

"Don't cry," said the man. "See, we both love the little bird, and I am going to show you something!"

He held the little dead sparrow close to his face, while the child watched, and breathed on it; something seemed to stir between his fingers, and when he opened his hand the bird flew away. Straight up in the air it flew, spreading its wings, and as the little sister looked up at it it seemed to change. She thought it had been brown, but now it was snow white all over, like a white dove, and it hovered a moment above them and then was gone, far up in the blue sky, but she thought she heard it singing as it flew.

The brother stared. "Where did it go?" he cried. "I saw it lying on your hand and then it wasn't there!"

"It flew away," said the little sister.

"It was dead," said her brother, "and dead things cannot fly."

"I tell you it flew," the little sister repeated. "It flew into the sky, and I saw it!"

And she came near and put her arms round the man's neck and kissed him. "You are a nice man," she said, "and you shall have all the flowers that I gather for Easter, for you are much nicer than Easter, and no one must ever be unkind to you, because I love you. And I want you to live with us always."

And she looked at him again, and this time she said, "I think you are Easter, for I see a shiny thing on your head."

But though the brother looked, he only saw the sun shining through the branches of the apple tree.

"You are a kind man," he said, "even if you aren't Easter, and some day I hope you will come again and tell us some more stories, for I like your stories very much. And when I grow up and have a sword of my own, I am going to give it to you."

They went home and left the man sitting there under the apple tree. His head leaned back against the tree trunk and his arms were outstretched and he seemed to be sleeping, and in his open hand lay the flowers the little sister had given him. But perhaps he was only resting, for he must have been very tired still.

"I tell you he is Easter," the little sister said. "He is just like I said he would be."

"He isn't Easter," said her brother, "but he is a very nice man, and I am sorry he has to walk so far."

But the little sister pulled at his hand, standing still in the road. "Don't you see?" she cried. "There is something shining round his head, like gold, and look—the apple tree is all in flower!"

The brother looked.

"It is only the setting sun," he said. "There is no blossom on the tree, for I looked this morning. But tomorrow we'll come back and see."

In the morning, when the children went back to look, the man had gone. But it was as the little sister had said; the apple tree that had been withered for so many years was in flower. The boughs, covered with pink and white blossoms, stretched out against the blue sky in blessing, and their perfume filled the air all about.

It was really Spring; the birds were singing and far away, as the children stood under the apple tree, they could hear the bells ringing for Easter.

BY MARGERY WILLIAMS BIANCO

THE SELFISH GIANT

Every afternoon, as they were coming from school, the children used to go and play in the Giant's garden.

It was a large, lovely garden, with soft green grass. Here and there over the grass stood beautiful flowers like stars, and there were twelve peach trees that in the springtime broke out into delicate blossoms of pink and pearl, and in the autumn bore rich fruit.

The birds sat on the trees and sang so sweetly that the children used to stop their games to listen to them. "How happy we are here!" they cried to each other.

One day the Giant came back. He had been to visit his friend, the Cornish ogre, and had stayed with him for seven years. After the seven years were over he had said all that he had to say, for his conversation was limited, and he determined to return to his own castle. When he arrived he saw the children playing in the garden.

"What are you doing here?" he cried in a very gruff voice, and the children ran away.

"My own garden is my own garden," said the Giant. "Anyone can understand that, and I will allow nobody to play in it but myself." So he built a high wall all around it, and put up a notice board: TRESPASSERS WILL BE PROSECUTED.

He was a very selfish giant.

The poor children had now nowhere to play. They tried to play on the road, but the road was very dusty and full of hard stones, and they did not like it. They used to wander round the high wall, when their lessons were over, and talk about the beautiful garden inside. "How happy we were there," they said to each other.

Then the Spring came, and all over the country there were little blossoms and little birds. Only in the garden of the Selfish Giant it was still Winter. The birds did not care to sing in it, as there were no children, and the trees forgot to blossom.

Once a beautiful flower put its head out from the grass, but when it saw the notice board it was so sorry for the children that it slipped back into the ground again, and went off to sleep. The only people who were pleased were the Snow and the Frost. "Spring has forgotten this garden," they cried, "so we will live here all the year round."

The Snow covered up the grass with her great white cloak, and the Frost painted all the trees silver. Then they invited the North Wind to stay with them, and he came. He was wrapped in furs, and he roared all day about the garden and blew the chimney pots down. "This is a delightful spot," he said; "we must ask the Hail on a visit."

So the Hail came. Every day for three hours he rattled on the roof of the castle till he broke most of the slates, and then he ran round and round the garden as fast as he could go. He was dressed in gray, and his breath was like ice.

"I cannot understand why the Spring is so late in coming," said the Selfish Giant, as he sat at the window and looked out at his cold white garden. "I hope the weather will change."

But the Spring never came, nor the Summer. The Autumn gave golden fruit to every garden, but to the Giant's garden she gave none. "He is too selfish," she said. So it was always Winter there, and the North Wind, and the Hail, and the Frost, and the Snow danced about through the trees.

One morning the Giant was lying awake in bed when he heard some lovely music. It sounded so sweet to his ears that he thought it must be the King's musicians passing by. It was really only a little linnet singing outside his window, but it was so long since he had heard a bird sing in his garden that it seemed to him to be the most beautiful music in the world.

Then the Hail stopped dancing over his head, and the North Wind ceased roaring, and a delicious perfume came to him through the open casement. "I believe the Spring has come at last," said the Giant, and he jumped out of bed and looked out.

What did he see?

He saw a most wonderful sight. Through a little hole in the wall the children had crept in, and they were sitting in the branches of the trees. In every tree that he could see, there was a little child. And the trees were so glad to have the children back again that they had covered themselves with blossoms and were waving their arms gently above the children's heads. The birds were flying about and twittering with delight, and the flowers were looking up through the green grass and laughing.

It was a lovely scene, only in one corner it was still Winter. It was the farthest corner of the garden, and in it was standing a little boy. He was so small that he could not reach up to the branches of the tree, and he was wandering all round it, crying bitterly. The poor tree was still quite covered with frost and snow, and the North Wind was blowing and roaring above it. "Climb up, little boy!" said the tree, and it bent its branches down as low as it could; but the boy was too tiny.

And the Giant's heart melted as he looked out. "How selfish I have been!" he said. "Now I know why the Spring would not come here. I will put that poor little boy on the top of the tree, and then I will knock down the wall, and my garden shall be the children's playground for ever and ever." He was really very sorry for what he had done.

So he crept downstairs and opened the front door quite softly and went out into the garden. But when the children saw him they were so frightened that they all ran away, and the garden became Winter again. Only the little boy did not run, for his eyes were so full of tears that he did not see the Giant coming. And the Giant strode up behind him and took him gently in his hand, and put him up into the tree.

The tree broke at once into blossom, and the birds came and sang on it, and the little boy stretched out his two arms and flung them around the Giant's neck, and kissed him. And the other children, when they saw that the Giant was not wicked any longer, came running back; and with them came the Spring.

"It is your garden now, little children," said the Giant, and he took a great axe and knocked down the wall. And when the people were going to market at twelve o'clock they found the Giant playing with the children in the most beautiful garden they had ever seen.

All day long they played, and in the evening they came to the Giant to bid him good-by.

"But where is your little companion," he said, "the boy I put into the tree?" The Giant loved him the best because he had kissed him.

"We don't know," answered the children. "He has gone away."

"You must tell him to be sure and come here tomorrow," said the Giant. But the children said that they did not know where he lived and had never seen him before; and the Giant felt very sad.

Every afternoon when school was over, the children came and played with the Giant. But the little boy whom the Giant loved was never seen again. The Giant was very kind to all the children, yet he longed for his first little friend and often spoke of him. "How I would like to see him!" he used to say.

Years went over, and the Giant grew very old and feeble. He could not play about any more, so he sat in a huge armchair, and watched the children at their games, and admired his garden. "I have many beautiful flowers," he said, "but the children are the most beautiful flowers of all."

One winter morning he looked out of his window as he was dressing. He did not hate the Winter now, for he knew that it was merely Spring asleep, and that the flowers were resting.

Suddenly he rubbed his eyes in wonder, and looked and looked. It certainly was a marvellous sight. In the farthest corner of the garden was a tree quite covered with lovely white blossoms. Its branches were all golden, and silver fruit hung down from them, and underneath it stood the little boy he had loved.

Downstairs ran the Giant, in great joy, and out into the garden. He hastened across and came near to the child. And when he came quite close his face grew red with anger, and he said, "Who hath dared to wound thee?" For on the palms of the child's hands were the prints of two nails, and the prints of two nails on the little feet.

"Who hath dared to wound thee?" cried the Giant. "Tell me, that I may take my big sword and slay him."

"Nay!" answered the child, "but these are the wounds of Love."

"Who art thou?" said the Giant, and a strange awe fell on him, and he knelt before the little child.

And the child smiled on the Giant and said to him, "You let me play once in your garden; today you shall come with me to my garden, which is Paradise."

And when the children ran in that afternoon, they found the Giant lying dead under the tree, all covered with white blossoms.

BY OSCAR WILDE

SECRETS AT THE MARDI GRAS

"Tomorrow is the day!" said Victor to his friend Emile. Hundreds of other children were saying the same thing in the city of New Orleans on the day before Mardi Gras.

Mardi Gras is Carnival time. Once a year the streets of New Orleans are transformed into a glowing pageant. There are masqueraders who dance in the public squares. Prancing horses and glittering floats parade through the town. There is even a mysterious King who rides on the most magnificent float of all.

Victor and Emile, like everyone in New Orleans, were counting the minutes until the Mardi Gras parade. The boys wondered what the floats would be like this year. The only people in the whole city who had seen the floats were the carpenters who had been working on them.

One of the rules of Mardi Gras is to keep the floats a secret. They are hidden in great empty warehouses along the river that are called the dens. Very few people know that the floats are hidden there.

Victor's father was one of the carpenters who worked in the dens. Everyone in the neighborhood was very proud of him and they all called him Papa Roland. Papa Roland had been working on the Mardi Gras floats for many years.

All of Victor's friends envied the little boy because he was allowed to visit the dens when he took Papa Roland his supper. Of course Victor could not go inside the dens. But he could go right up to the big front door where Old Jacques sat smoking his corncob pipe and keeping guard.

Tonight was the last night Victor would visit the dens. By

tomorrow the work on the floats would be all finished. As Victor started off with Papa Roland's lunchbox, Emile walked beside him.

"What's the big float going to be like this year?" Emile asked Victor.

Victor looked surprised at Emile's question. "I don't know, Emile," he said. "It is a surprise."

"You ought to know," said Emile. "Your father works on the big float every day. Hasn't he told you what it looks like?"

"Of course not," said Victor. "Everybody knows that the big float must be kept a secret until the day of Mardi Gras. My father would never tell."

Emile did not ask any more questions because Pierre, the vegetable man, was standing near. Emile knew that Pierre would tell him to stop teasing Victor. Pierre's cart blocked the sidewalk while Pierre waited for the woman in the top balcony of an old house to lower a bucket on a rope.

"Onions and tomatoes," she called out to the vegetable man.

Pierre filled the bucket with the vegetables and his customer pulled them up to the balcony. She looked over her purchase and sent down the money. Pierre thanked her and moved off with his cart.

"Victor," said Emile, now that Pierre was out of the way, "I dare you to go into the dens and find out what the big float looks like."

"But Emile, nobody is allowed in the dens," protested Victor.

"I double-dare you," said Emile, "but perhaps you are afraid."

Victor's brown eyes looked troubled. "No, Emile, I am not afraid," he said, "but I should not like to break the rule of Mardi Gras. You know that no one must see the floats before the parade."

"If you will get inside the dens, I'll buy you four snowballs," said Emile. "I have the money right here. You know how good they are."

Victor thought about the cold, sweet taste of snowballs. These are ices dipped in syrup and sold in New Orleans. Imagine having four snowballs all to himself! He began to wonder if he could fool Emile by saying he had been in the dens, even if he did not go all the way in. That would be a lie. While he was wondering if he should tell a lie, Emile said:

"You must bring me proof you have been in the dens, Victor. And when I see the proof I will buy you the four snowballs. What do you say?"

Victor thought about the snowballs and nodded his head. "All right, Emile," he said. "I will bring you a tiny piece of the decorations on the big float."

"Word of honor?" said Emile.

"Word of honor," said Victor, and the two boys shook hands on it. Victor was very thoughtful after that. He knew he must do his best to keep his word. But he also knew how hard it was going to be to get into the closely guarded dens. When he saw the high windows in the warehouse, he decided that the only way he could get in would be with the help of his friend, the guard.

Old Jacques sat on a keg in front of the door, smoking his corncob pipe and keeping watch.

"Good evening, Jacques," said Victor.

"*Bonsoir,*" said Jacques, saying good evening in French. Old Jacques lived in the French Quarter in New Orleans. He was partly French and still spoke French along with English. There are many French families living in this Old Quarter. It looks like a part of the old France across the sea. The houses have court-yards and balconies and beautiful walled gardens.

"You have your papa's supper, I see," said Jacques. "That is good. They are working hard in there to finish the floats. To-morrow is the day. Think of it. Thirty men hard at work since last spring and now it is February. But it is worth all the hard work. Wait until you see the big float. It is a beauty!"

"Emile and I were wondering," Victor said, "if there is any way we could see the big float *sooner* than tomorrow?"

"What!" cried Jacques. "What are you saying, little Victor?"

"If you would just let me in for a peek," said Victor.

"Saints above!" cried Jacques, waving his pipe in the air. "You know I cannot let you look in the dens. I will take you down to the wharves to see the banana boats unload. I will show you the most beautiful garden in New Orleans with a fountain and magnolia trees and a hanging balcony made of lacy wrought iron. I will even take you on a picnic in the Bayou country where the pirates used to hide. But a peek in the den. No, no! Everyone in New Orleans knows the meaning of the words—Not until the day—"

"Who decided that everything must be kept a secret until the day of Mardi Gras?" Emile asked.

"The secrets of the Mardi Gras have been handed down for generations," said Old Jacques. "Our grandfathers brought the custom from France where Mardi Gras is a feast day. It falls on Shrove Tuesday or Fat Tuesday, as the French call it. It is the day the French peasants lead a fat ox through the village streets to remind the people that this is the last day they can eat meat until Easter."

"Did the French peasants have a Carnival as big as ours?" said Victor.

"No, indeed," said Old Jacques. "Mardi Gras is celebrated more magnificently in New Orleans than in any other place in the world."

"And this year it will be more magnificent than ever," said a happy voice in the doorway. The voice belonged to Papa Roland, who had come up from the dens to get his lunchbox. He smiled at the two boys. "You just wait and see," he said.

When Papa Roland went back inside, Old Jacques began to move the barrels in the yard into the den.

"What are you doing that for?" said Emile.

"These barrels are going to be the seats on the floats," said Old Jacques. "They will be decorated so beautifully that you will never know them when you see them tomorrow."

The next time Jacques carried a barrel into the den, Victor ran as fast as he could to the barrels that were left in the yard. Quick as a wink the boy was in a barrel. He had found a way to get into the dens!

"Emile," he called as he pulled down the lid of the barrel, "Run away quickly before Jacques comes back and sees there is only one of us."

"Good luck," Emile called, and hurried off as fast as he could.

The barrel was quite small. There was not much room to stretch in. Victor held his breath. He was afraid if he took a deep breath he would split the sides of the barrel. How dark it was! And how still! He wondered how long he would have to stay in the tiny place.

After a while he heard Jacques come back. Then he felt the barrel moving. Up! Up!

Jacques groaned. "My, what a weight. I must be getting old," the old man said, as he carried the barrel across the yard and into the doorway of the dens.

Victor heard the sound of Jacques' footsteps on the wooden floor. Then he felt the barrel being lowered. Down! Down! He heard Jacques going away. And he heard the sound of men's voices and the creaking of saws and the tap-tap of hammers. There was a tiny knothole in the barrel and Victor put one eye to the small opening. He saw Jacques' legs move up the steps. And he saw the legs of the workmen in the shadows. That was all he could see.

It was so warm inside the barrel the little boy began to feel very sleepy. He must have fallen asleep because the next thing he knew there was not a sound to be heard anywhere in the dens. All the hammers had stopped. Even the lights were out.

Victor pushed up the lid of the barrel. All the men had gone home. He was alone in the dens. His legs were stiff and cramped but he managed to climb out of the barrel.

High up in the walls of the warehouse there were little windows.

Silvery moonlight shone through the windows. There was something big and shiny in the middle of the room, something that looked as if it were covered with silver moonlight.

As Victor came closer to it, he saw it was a float! An enormous float. A float that looked like a giant wedding cake, covered with tinsel and flowers. There was a throne in the center of the float. This was the big float, then, the biggest and most beautiful of all the floats. It was the one that Rex, the King of the Carnival, would ride in tomorrow.

Victor felt as if he were dreaming. He was almost afraid to reach out his hand and touch the shining carriage for fear it would dissolve into moonlight. He walked round and round the float, feasting his eyes on it. How wonderful it was! Then he remembered that he must bring Emile something from the float to prove that he had really seen it.

There was a pretty border of silver leaves around the edge of the float. Victor was very careful not to spoil the border. He chose a tiny silver leaf from 'way in the back where it wouldn't be missed. A cluster of leaves covered the spot where the little leaf had been. Victor put the leaf into his pocket and then, with a last look at the dazzling float, ran up the stairs and out the door into the night.

When he got home he found that no one had missed him because his family was getting ready for Mardi Gras. His mother was far too busy to ask any questions. She was putting the finishing touches on the goblin costume he was going to wear the next day.

Victor stole softly off to bed. He hid the little silver leaf under his pillow to keep it safe till morning.

The day dawned bright and fair. Victor woke up with a start when he heard the sound of pebbles on his window. He looked out and saw a row of goblins. They all wore masks. One goblin had a red suit, one had a green suit, and the third had a yellow suit. The red goblin jumped and somersaulted and was as gay as a circus clown. "Hurry up, hurry up," the red goblin called.

Victor recognized Emile's voice. "I'll be right down," he said.

Victor's mother helped him put on the bright purple goblin suit she had made for him. Purple was one of the Carnival colors. The whole town would be decorated with green, yellow, and purple bunting and flags, the three colors that mean Mardi Gras.

When Papa Roland saw the four little goblins he said: "I'll wager the four of you will make a chain and push your way right up in front at the parade."

Making a chain is the children's way of getting a good view of the floats. They all join hands and push their way together through the crowds. Papa Roland was right. This was just what the four goblins planned to do.

"Have a good time," Papa Roland said. "Just wait till you see the big float!"

"I've already seen it," Victor whispered to Emile. "Look, I have brought you a silver leaf from it."

"When you show me the place where the silver leaf came from, I shall buy you the snowballs," Emile promised.

The four goblins dashed off, darting in and out of the crowds, stopping to stare at pretty girls selling flowers, peddlers offering spun candy, colored dusters, bags of peanuts and popcorn, and bright clouds of balloons. Bells tinkled. Horns blew. Everyone in the street wore a mask. There were masks that looked like the heads of animals. There were clowns and grinning skulls and devils with horns.

All the masqueraders were laughing and singing as they made their way toward Canal Street where Rex, the King of the Carnival, would lead the parade of floats later in the day.

Down near the river there were sounds of further merriment. Four brightly dressed goblins in a row arrived just in time to see the Zulu King ride up in a gaily decorated river barge.

The Zulu King was a joke. He was all dressed up in a grass skirt and a fur vest, with a broomstick for a sceptre and a tin crown on his head. He left the barge and climbed into a mule cart while the crowd cheered and laughed. When the Zulu Queen joined him, trailing her robes of purple, everyone laughed harder than ever, including the four goblins.

Now it was time to go back to Canal Street and wait for the big parade. The boys walked through streets that were seething with color and song. Hundreds of visitors had come to town to join in the fun. They were dressed as gypsies, pirates, knights, and lovely ladies.

Victor felt as if he were walking in dreamland instead of in the familiar city of New Orleans.

At last a loud cheer rose from the crowd. "Here it comes! Here comes the parade!"

Mounted policemen cleared the way for the royal attendants of King Rex. They came riding in splendor on spirited horses. They carried swords like shining tongues of flame and they were dressed in purple and gold.

"It is time to make a chain," cried Emile, and leading the way he plunged through the crowd and found a place for all four goblins right in front where they would get a good view.

At last the moment they had been waiting for arrived. A shining mass of color and dancing light appeared in the distance. It was the beautiful float that Victor had seen the night before in the den. High on the golden throne sat King Rex, smiling and nodding behind his mask. No one knew who he was. He would wear the mask until sundown and then he would disclose his identity.

All masks were removed at dusk. This was one of the customs of Mardi Gras. In the ancient days there were dangers in meeting masked men after dark. A mask could easily hide the face of the enemy. So the rule was made that at Carnival time the masks must come off at sundown.

The float was so high it seemed to reach almost up to the over-hanging balconies that lined the street. It was as beautiful as a spun sugar cake and glittering with jewels and silver. 'Way down at the bottom, almost within reach of their hands, the boys saw the border of silver leaves that matched the silver leaf Victor held in his hand.

"You see, Emile," Victor said shyly, "I really saw the float last night."

"Yes, you did," Emile smiled, "and I'll buy you the snowballs I promised you."

There was so much to look at, the boys could hardly remember just what they saw when the floats had passed them. The King wore a cape embroidered in gold and the gold fringe trailing from it must have been yards long. The Queen was dressed in gleaming white satin and her gloves and her cape were sparkling with jewels.

Following the big float were dozens of other floats, swaying under the weight of flowers and ornaments and laughing masqueraders. When the parade had passed, everyone crowded into the street again and there was music and dancing and singing as the Carnival kept on going.

Soon the four goblins went in search of the snowball man. They found him pushing his little cart through the crowds. The cart had a gay awning top. Emile bought the four snowballs he had promised to Victor.

"One for each of us," said Victor, and the four boys feasted in silence. The snowballs were so good, no one had a word to say until the last sweet cold drop was gone.

All afternoon the merrymakers played in the streets of New Orleans. In the Vieux Carré, the French name for the Old Quarter of town, there were contests and prizes for the best costumes. At dusk the electric lights were turned on and Canal Street was filled with twinkling colored stars. The balconies were crowded with people and the street was lined with weary merrymakers as the time drew nearer for the torchlight procession of Comus, the last and favorite of all the kings of Mardi Gras. Comus was known to everyone as the god of festival, of joy, and of mirth.

Once more Emile led his friends through the crowd to a front-row place on the curb.

The sound of far-off music came nearer and nearer. Then, out of the soft dusk, the bobbing flares of light began to appear, circles of pale fire surrounded by plumes of smoke rising above the red-robed men who carried the torches.

Thirty men circled the golden coach of Comus so that the beloved ruler of the festival seemed to be riding in a girdle of fire. The torches shone on the golden throne and the golden sceptre. This shining spectacle was the most beautiful sight of Mardi Gras.

Then came the exciting moment when the maskers on the floats reached into tiny silk bags and brought forth presents to be tossed into the crowd. How everyone shouted and clapped and cried, "Please—throw me something," as chains and strings of beads and bracelets and bags of candy rained down on them.

Victor held out his hands and called "Please—" just as the others were doing. One of the maskers saw him and called out: "Here! A prize for the little purple goblin. Catch it!"

Victor felt his feet leave the ground. He jumped as high as he could, and the pretty golden chain that sailed through the air landed right in his hand, though dozens of other hands reached for it too. He was so happy he could hardly say, "Thank you." This was the most wonderful Mardi Gras he could remember. He had even got a prize.

The procession moved on, each float more beautiful than the one before. Swans, butterflies, and stags led the floats through the torch-lit street. Shadows danced. Flowers nodded. There was a sleepy dreamlike quality to this night-time Mardi Gras parade.

The four goblins followed the floats to the Opera House where King Comus and his Queen would join King Rex and his Queen at the ball that would last until midnight.

The boys watched the beautiful figures leave the floats and go in through the wide doors of the great hall where the dance was held. They heard the swinging music of the orchestra. Then they saw the torchbearers put out the flares and the floats moved off into the night.

The lights on Canal Street twinkled at the four goblins as they trudged homeward. They felt the cool river breeze on their flushed cheeks. Their feet were very tired. They had walked miles and miles that day.

Ah, how wonderful Mardi Gras was! They went to bed to dream of the parades they had seen, the processions of floats and masqueraders, the color and the beauty that belonged to Mardi Gras. Outside the night was soft and still. The music was only an echo. It was midnight and Mardi Gras was over until another year.

BY JOAN AND JOSEPHINE COSTANTINO

THE PASSION PLAY OF OBERAMMERGAU

High in the Bavarian Alps of Germany is the little town of Oberammergau. It lies along either side of the banks of the Ammer River from which it takes its name. Although Oberammergau is enjoyed both as a summer and a winter resort it becomes extremely popular every ten years. For it is then that the most famous of all Passion Plays is performed—The Passion Play of Oberammergau.

It all began over three hundred years ago. It was the year 1633 and a terrible plague was raging in the country. Many of the villagers of Oberammergau had been stricken and it seemed as if nothing could stop the spread of the fatal sickness. But finally it was over and those who survived took a vow. In gratitude for having come safely through the ordeal they promised that every ten years they would honor the Passion of Christ by giving a play depicting his last days on earth.

A few miles from Oberammergau is the monastery of Ettal and it is thought that the first Passion Play was written by one of the monks. It is known that the music which is still used was composed in 1814 by the schoolmaster of Oberammergau, Rochus Dedler. The Play however has had some changes made from time to time.

Although the first performance of The Passion Play was given in 1634, it was later changed so it would fall in 1680 and since that time has always been performed every tenth year. There have been three interruptions. The first was in 1870 due to the Franco-Prussian War. Again it was postponed in 1920 on account of World War I, and the last time in 1940 because of World War II.

For generations the people of Oberammergau have grown up dedicated to the tradition of this performance. During the years in between they work at their trades. Many of them are skilled craftsmen and their woodcarvings are some of the finest in the world. One of their specialties is the making of rosaries, crucifixes, and images of the Saints.

As the year draws near when The Passion Play is to be given, preparations begin. The people of Oberammergau are deeply religious and plan reverently each little detail. Even in the years between, the men wear their beards and hair long so that neither wigs nor makeup will be worn for the performance.

Choosing the cast of characters is a very serious undertaking. A committee to do this is selected first. This is made up of the burgomaster, the village council, the priest, and other members selected by the people. There are strict requirements for participation in the Play. The persons taking part must first of all be of fine moral character. Secondly, they must be able to act. Of course they must be natives of Oberammergau. And lastly, the women may not be married.

To be chosen to portray the character of Christ or of Mary is

the highest honor a person may receive. And yet when the decisions of the commitee have been made known they are accepted without question. Seven hundred performers take part and this number includes the orchestra and chorus.

After the committee has announced the names of the cast, preparations begin in earnest. Besides rehearsals there is much work to be done. Costumes must be looked over, for many of them will have to be made anew. Some of the properties may have to be replaced. And of course the whole town must prepare for thousands of visitors who will flock to the village to see the performance. It is estimated that during the season, which lasts from May until September, more than three hundred thousand persons visit Oberammergau.

In 1930 a new theater was constructed for The Passion Play. The audience occupies an auditorium which seats over six thousand persons. The Play is performed on a large open-air platform and the audience views it through an oval arch. It is a long play lasting all day with about a two-hour intermission at lunch time.

The Passion Play is not, as some people think, a portrayal of the entire life of Christ. Instead it depicts just His last days on earth. It begins with His triumphal entry into Jerusalem on Palm Sunday and ends with His ascension into heaven. Preceding each act is a tableau portraying a scene from the Old Testament. A chorus explains how this incident from Old Testament history has its parallel in the New Testament story of the life of Christ.

Persons who have witnessed this dramatic portrayal of Christ's suffering have found it a most moving experience.

There are other German towns which have given Passion Plays too. And since 1938 at Spearfish, South Dakota, a group of people who came to this country from Germany have given one each year. But none of them has ever been as famous as the one given in Oberammergau, the little village in the Bavarian Alps.

BY JANETTE WOOLSEY

THE LITTLE WHITE LILY

Story of the Easter Seal

The little white lily, on a tiny paper seal, has traveled out on its mission to millions every year at Easter time, carrying its message. Here is the story of that lily and its message.

There was once a little crippled boy named Jimmy. He had come to the Elyria Memorial Hospital in Ohio because the surgeon there thought he could be helped. But Jimmy was not so hopeful. "I'm a cripple," he said bitterly. "They can't help me!"

One day a man stopped in to see and talk with him. Taking the little boy's hand in his, he pressed it hard and said earnestly, "Jimmy, you can walk again if you'll only try! You've just got to try!" The man talked to the boy again and again, and Jimmy did try. The two became fast friends. Soon Jimmy was calling the man "Daddy Allen."

Daddy Allen had a story of his own. Back in 1907 when his son was eighteen years old, the boy had been crippled in a trolley-car accident. After an operation, his son died. Edgar F. Allen realized that the boy's death had been caused by the lack of needed equipment at the local hospital. He tried to think of what could be done to prevent such tragedies as this from happening. He began at once to spend his entire time and all his energies in raising money for a modern well-equipped hospital. The following year the Elyria Memorial Hospital opened its doors to the community. It was here that Jimmy had come as a patient.

Jimmy did learn to walk again. One day the surgeon, Dr. Baldwin, and Mr. Allen stood watching the little boy struggling valiantly to walk the length of the hospital corridor. Suddenly the surgeon made a remark to Mr. Allen that was to change the lives of millions of crippled children.

"Mr. Allen," Dr. Baldwin said, "you have done so much for this hospital. Why don't you turn your attention now to crippled children? I know there are many of them, and they need you as a friend."

That is how Mr. Edgar F. Allen became Daddy Allen to many hundreds of crippled children like Jimmy. For the greathearted man *did* center his attention on this vast new idea. He began in his own county, where two hundred crippled children were found to reside. Through his efforts the Gates Memorial Hospital for Crippled Children was opened in 1915. The hospital was equipped to handle forty-five children, with a fine staff of doctors and nurses. Everything was shiny and new and ready to take over the care of those who so badly needed help. But, to everyone's surprise, the children simply did not come to the hospital. Daddy Allen could not understand it. Why did they not come?

The answer, he found, was with the parents of the children. Many of them dreaded to be separated from their handicapped sons and daughters. Some were afraid of the expense that would be involved. But most of all, they were ashamed to let it be known that their little boy or girl was physically crippled! Up to this time it had been the custom for families to keep their crippled children apart from normal ways of life. This was an old, old belief that went back hundreds of years.

Mr. Allen knew something of the history of this attitude, the lack of care, that had been accepted by families in regard to their handicapped members. He knew that in ancient times some nations, like Sparta, had even killed their citizens who were physically imperfect. In the Middle Ages, this practice was no longer followed, but the persons who were crippled were usually an object of ridicule, and sometimes were considered insane. It was not until 1780 that an institution in Orbe, Switzerland, was established solely for the purpose of giving physical care to persons who were disabled. Then in Munich, Germany, a home for the

[243]

crippled was opened which was the first to give not only physical care but education as well. This was an immense difference, for up to that time no one had thought of the handicapped as teachable. Schools similar to the one in Munich began to appear in Europe and in the United States. Disabled persons at last were being given the chance to learn, and some adults became self-supporting.

But the old custom of keeping handicapped children at home without special training was a hard one to overcome. This is what Daddy Allen and the others in Elyria were up against when they opened their new hospital for crippled children. How could the people be taught to face this problem? Money was needed. To obtain the money, communities needed to know the facts. Mr. Allen began to talk of his project wherever the people would listen—YMCA's, Chambers of Commerce, women's clubs, and finally the clubs whose purpose is to serve the community. Here at last his story aroused interest. When he approached the Rotary Clubs, he found the support he needed. In 1919 the Ohio Society for Crippled Children was formed in Elyria. One of the purposes of the organization was as follows: "To assist in solving problems incident to the raising of funds as well as the building, equipping, and maintaining of hospitals for the care and cure of crippled children."

The Ohio Plan, as it was known, soon spread to other states, largely through the efforts of Mr. Allen and the Rotarians. Plans for a national organization soon began to take shape. The District Governors of Rotary Club gave their wholehearted support to the plan. In October of 1921 at a meeting in Toledo, Ohio, the National Society for Crippled Children was launched. "Daddy" Allen was its president. In 1923 a magazine called *The Crippled Child* started publication. In 1944, to the title "The National Society for Crippled Children," the words "and Adults" were added. In 1953 the Easter Seal Research Foundation was established.

But what about the little white lily? It began in this way. In the depression of the 1930's the National Society, along with other organizations, was facing serious financial troubles in carrying out its work. It was decided that the public should be asked for contributions. The sale of seals was suggested. Mr. Paul H. King was chairman of the finance committee.

"We suggest Easter as the time for the sale of the seals," he said, speaking before the National convention. "Thoughts of Easter and the crippled child harmonize wonderfully. Easter means, of course, Resurrection and New Life; and certainly the rehabilitation of crippled children means new life and activity, complete or partial, physically, mentally, and spiritually."

All of the states did not adopt the Easter Seal plan immediately. Kentucky, however, carried out a very successful campaign with Easter Seals in 1934. In this first year of the adoption of the Easter Seal plan, twenty-eight thousand dollars was raised. This experience gave the National Society the encouragement it needed to make the Easter Seal campaign a successful annual event.

Each year the seal, with its symbolic white lily, adopted in 1952, and the picture of some chosen handicapped child, goes by mail into millions of homes throughout the nation. Today the Easter Seal work is a national project of the National Society for Crippled Children and Adults. It is carried on in the fifty states of the United States, the District of Columbia, and Puerto Rico. There are more than fourteen hundred centers and programs for care and treatment of crippled children and adults.

The Easter Seal Society is the largest voluntary agency in the world serving the crippled. More than 132,000 children in one year are helped to walk, talk, and live like other children. Over 26,000 adults in one year are helped to become independent in spite of their handicaps.

"More has been accomplished for the crippled in this single generation than in all of the generations of man's civilization before our time."

As the seal with the little white lily goes forth each Easter time, it is remindful of a New Life and a New Beginning that will come to many because of its wonderful message.

BY ELIZABETH HOUGH SECHRIST

INDEX

Alden, Raymond Macdonald, 176-183
Andersen, Hans Christian, 198-201
Anemone legend, 86
APPLE TREE, THE, 209-220
Ash Wednesday, 35-36; in Austria, 35; in Germany, 35; in Spain, 36
Aspen tree legend, 88
Ass legend, 74
At Easter Time, 148

Bach, Johann Sebastian, 111-115
Ballad of Trees and the Master, 151
Bianco, Margery Williams, 209-220
Bigham, Madge, 184-188
Blanden, Charles G., 141
Blini, 33
Bollers, 33
Bowring, Sir John, 128-129
BOY WHO DISCOVERED THE SPRING, THE, 176-183
BRINGING IN THE SPRING, 202-208
Butterfly legend, 83

Calendar, 22
CANDLES AT MIDNIGHT, 189-197
Carnivals, 33-34; *see also* Mardi Gras
"Clipping the church," 47
Colum, Padraic, 170-175
Costantino, Joan and Josephine, 228-238
Cross, Symbol of, 72
Customs, Easter, 31-67: Hebrew, 62; in Albania, 51; in America, 27,
    56-59, 67; in Ancient Rome, 62; in Armenia, 46; in Austria, 63; in
    Belgium, 49, 62; in Bulgaria, 65; in Czechoslovakia, 51, 65; in Den-
    mark, 33; in Egypt, 62; in England, 47, 62, 63; in Finland, 52; in
    France, 25, 49, 63; in Germany, 49, 62, 63, 67; in Greece, 25, 51, 62,
    65; in Hungary, 25, 52; in Ireland, 47, 63; in Italy, 49-51, 63-65; in
    Jerusalem, 46; in Latvia, 52; in Mexico, 54; in Norway, 33, 52, 67;
    in Persia, 62; in Poland, 25; in Rumania, 52, 65; in Russia, 51; in
    Scotland, 47; in Slavic countries, 25; in South America, 53; in Spain,

52; in Sweden, 52; in Switzerland, 49, 62; in the Ukraine, 51, 65; in the Tyrol, 63; in Yugoslavia, 65; Puritan, 25

Dogwood tree legend, 89

Eagle legend, 79
Easter: date, 22; history, 21-27; legends, 23; lights, 23
Easter bells, 40, 49
Easter egg rolling, 67
Easter egg trees, 67
Easter eggs, 39, 51, 52, 60-67
Easter in the Woods, 145
Easter Morn, 154
Easter Octave, 25
Easter rabbit, 60-62
Easter seals, 242-247
Easter vigil, 24
Easter Week, 149
Eastre, 21, 27
Egg legend, 83; *see also* Easter eggs
Epitaphios, 42
EVEN UNTO THE END OF THE WORLD, 159-169

Fairy stones of Virginia legend, 90
Fastelaven, 33
Fastnachts, 33, 56
Fat Tuesday, 33
Fauré, Jean-Baptiste, 37, 124-125
Fisher, Aileen, 154
Flower Sunday, 53
Frost, Frances, 145
Frost, Robert, 142

Good Friday, 41-43: in America, 59; in Bulgaria, 42; in Czechoslovakia, 42; in England, 42, 43; in Germany, 41; in Greece, 42; in Italy, 41; in Mexico, 41, 54; in Monaco, 42; in South America, 41, 53; in Spain, 41; in Yugoslavia, 42
Green Things Growing, 144
Green Thursday, 39

Handel, George Frideric, 105-110
Hawthorne legend, 85
Hinkson, Katharine Tynan, 150

Holy Grail, *see* Quest of the Holy Grail; *see also* PARSIFAL

Holy Thursday, 39-40: in Armenia, 39; in Belgium, 49; in England, 39; in Germany, 39; in Holland, 39; in Hungary, 39; in Mexico, 54; in South America, 53; in Syria, 39; in the Ukraine, 39

Holy Saturday, 44-45: in Austria, 44; in Bulgaria, 45; in Czechoslovakia, 45; in Germany, 44; in Holland, 45; in Hungary, 45; in Italy, 45; in Mexico, 54; in Poland, 45; in Rumania, 44

Holy Sepulchre, Shrine of the, 41

Holy Week, 37

Hot cross buns, 42-43

Housman, A. E., 146

Ilex legend, 84

In the Cross of Christ I Glory, 128-129

Jesus Christ Is Ris'n Today, 132-133

Jewett, Eleanore M., 159-169

Joy, 153

Kelsey, Alice Geer, 189-197

Kingsley, Charles, 149

Lanier, Sidney, 151

Legends, Easter, 71-90

Lengten-tid, 31

Lent, 31-45

Lent Lily, The, 146

"Lifting," 47

Lion legend, 75

LITTLE WHITE LILY, THE, 242-247

LOVELIEST ROSE IN THE WORLD, THE, 198-201

Mardi Gras, 33, 56; *see also* Carnivals

Maugham, Henry Neville, 145

Maundy Thursday *see* Holy Thursday

MESSIAH, 105-110

Milman, Henry Hart, 126-127

Mulock, Dinah Marie, 144

Music, Easter, 103-137

My Faith Looks Up to Thee, 130-131

Nicea, Council of, 22, 62

Night of illumination, 44

Oberammergau *see* PASSION PLAY OF OBERAMMERGAU, THE
Opera, 104
Oratorios, 104
Origin of the Easter Lilies, The, 152
Owl legend, 80

Palestrina, 135-137
Palm Sunday, 37-38: in Austria, 37; in Finland, 37; in Italy, 37; in Mexico, 37; in Slavic countries, 37; in South America, 53; in Yugoslavia, 38
Palm tree legend, 87
Palmer, Ray, 130-131
Palms, The, 37, 124-125
Pancake Day, 31; *see also* Shrove Tuesday
Paques, 21
PARSIFAL, 116-123
Paschal candle, 24, 44
Paschal egg, 62
Pascua, 21, 53
Paske, 52
Pasos, 41
Pasqua, 21
Pasque, 141
Passion Music, 104
PASSION PLAY OF OBERAMMERGAU, THE, 239-241
Passion Week, 53; *see also* Holy Week
Pesach, 21
Phoenix legend, 78
Pomegranate legend, 86
Pott, Francis, 135
Prayer in Spring, A, 142
Pretzels, 35

Quest of the Holy Grail legend, 91-99

Rabbit legend, 77; *see also* Easter rabbits
Radica, 34
Reed legend, 85
Richards, Laura E., 148
Ride On, Ride On in Majesty, 126-127
Robin legend, 81

Sabin, Edwin L., 147
ST. JOHN PASSION, 41, 59

INDEX

ST. MATTHEW PASSION, 37, 41, 111-115

Scorpion legend, 84

SECRETS AT THE MARDI GRAS, 227-238

SELFISH GIANT, THE, 221-226

Seven Last Words, The, 59

Sheep and Lambs, 150

Shrove Tuesday, 31-34: in America, 56; in Austria, 33; in England, 31; in Estonia, 33; in Finland, 33; in France, 33; in Germany, 33; in Norway, 33; in South America, 53; in Switzerland, 33

Song, 141

Song, 145

Song of Easter, 143

Strife Is O'er, The, 135-137

Swallow legend, 82

Symbols, Easter, 71-90

Thaxter, Celia, 143

Thistle legend, 84

Tomb, Symbol of, 73

Wagner, Richard, 116-123

Wesley, Charles, 132-133

Whale, Symbol of, 76

WHITE BLACKBIRD, THE, 170-175

WHY THE IVY IS ALWAYS GREEN, 184-188

Wilde, Oscar, 153, 221-226

Willow Sunday, 37

Yates, Elizabeth, 202-208

Young, Ella, 141

ABOUT THE AUTHORS

Elizabeth Hough Sechrist became interested in writing for children while she was a children's librarian in Bethlehem, Pennsylvania. Each year she was asked by boys and girls, teachers and librarians for information on Christmas in other lands. Because of the lack of material, she began to collect and write on the subject herself, and the resulting book, *Christmas Everywhere,* has been popular in schools and libraries for many years.

After nine years' experience in Bethlehem and Pittsburgh libraries, Mrs. Sechrist gave up her work to devote her time to writing, editing, and lecturing on children's books—and incidentally to keeping house. At Spring Meadow Farm in York County, Pennsylvania, where she and her husband live, a collection of cookbooks is conspicuous on the shelves along with those on birds, animals, and furniture. Spring Meadow Farm is a lively place with its sheep, lambs, cocker spaniels, cats and kittens, ducks and geese.

And yet amidst all this activity, Mrs. Sechrist finds time to write books—although she claims the days are never long enough!

Janette Woolsey is a librarian at the Martin Memorial Library in York, Pennsylvania. One summer her library program was a marionette theatre, and it was during this time that she became interested in play production and writing. She and the children wrote the plays and presented them to a capacity audience each week. Miss Woolsey is a graduate of Middlebury College, Pratt Institute, and Columbia University. She started her library career as children's librarian at Ohio University. She lives in York, and devotes much of her free time to lecturing about children's books and storytelling.